GP RECRUITMENT

Survival Guide to the GPST / GPVTS Selection Centre

Author: Gail Allsopp

Published by:

ISC Medical, an imprint and trading name of Interview Skills Consulting ltd

Suite 434, Hamilton House, Mabledon Place, London WC1H 9BB
www.iscmedical.co.uk - Tel: 0845 226 9487

First Edition: October 2007
Reprinted: June 2008
ISBN13: 978-1-905812-14-1
A catalogue record for this book is available from the British Library.

Printed in the United Kingdom by:
Aidan's Ltd. Reg. Office 35 Ballards Lane, London N3 1XW

ISCMEDICAL
Interview Skills Consulting

For my dad.

Remember, silence is not always golden!

Interview Skills Consulting

Acknowledgements

I would like to thank Mr Nikos Karamalikis for his contribution to the book.

Contents

	Page
Introduction	7
About the Author	9
The Selection Centre	10
Set-up and Practical Advice	11
Assessment Criteria	17
Section 1 – The Simulated Patient / Role Play	19
Section 2 – Role-Play Practice Scenarios	37
Practice Role Play 1	43
Practice Role Play 2	53
Practice Role Play 3	63
Practice Role Play 4	75
Practice Role Play 5	89
Section 3 – Group Discussions	119
Section 4 – Group Discussion. Practice Scenarios	123
Group Discussion. Scenario 1 (Simple)	127
Group Discussion. Scenario 2 (Extended Simple - Presentation)	135
Group Discussion. Scenario 3 (Extended Complicated)	147
Group Discussion. Scenario 4 (Role-orientated)	161
Group Discussion. Scenario 5 (Simple)	169
Section 5 – Task Prioritisation Written Exercise	177
Section 6 – Task Prioritisation. Practice Exercises	197
Task Prioritisation. Practice Exercise 1 (Simple)	199
Task Prioritisation. Practice Exercise 2 (Advanced)	219
Task Prioritisation. Practice Exercise 3 (Advanced)	237
Task Prioritisation. Practice Exercise 4 (10-minute OSCE)	253
Section 7 – Final words	267
Summary of topics covered	268
Summary of proposed assessment criteria	270
Summary of topics covered within the text	272
Summary of other topics that could be used	273
Disclaimer	274
References	275
Summary of abbreviations used	276
Index of figures in the text	277

Definition of stages of assessment

The recruitment into GP Specialist Training consists of three main stages:

Stage 1: the online application process
A basic application form designed to check your eligibility for entering the General Practice training programme. All eligible candidates are invited to the next stage.

Stage 2: the examination-based assessment
Includes two papers (90 minutes each):

- Paper 1 – Clinical Problem Solving. Includes Extended Matching Questions (EMQs) and Multiple-Choice Questions (MCQs, usually Best of Five format). This paper is designed to test whether you have acquired the basic clinical knowledge and judgement required of a GP trainee.

- Paper 2 – Situational Judgement Test (SJT) / Professional Dilemmas. This checks your suitability for General Practice training from the point of view of your personal attributes.

Those who score highest will be invited to the Stage 3 assessment centre.

Stage 3: the assessment centre
This is a one-day assessment of your skills and competencies, using, in most cases, the following three activities:

- Role play (simulated patient consultation)
- Group discussion
- Written prioritisation task

Introduction

I would like to say "Congratulations!" to those of you who have bought this book in preparation for the Stage 3 assessment centre after successfully completing the Stage 2 examination for General Practice training. You are now over halfway through the selection process and getting ever closer to securing the most wonderful job in the world.

If you are reading this prior to Stage 2, good luck with the exam. You will find that some of the ethical information in this book may be relevant to the Stage 2 assessment. However, most of the Stage 2 questions are clinically based, and I would therefore suggest that you concentrate on passing Stage 2 before embarking on reading the rest of this book.

There is always a great deal of anxiety surrounding the General Practice specialist training (GPST) application process, particularly after the complications encountered in early 2007 with the online MTAS (Medical Training Application Service) system. Please be assured that the GP assessment and selection process is very robust, fair, extensively tried and tested and designed to appoint the best candidates.

Don't panic, and don't allow yourself to become caught up in the frenzy of the process. Be confident in your own ability and be assured that you can secure that training post by understanding the process, identifying your own strengths and weaknesses, confirming your strengths and working to improve those weaknesses by completing adequate preparation.

By the end of the book I would hope that you feel much better informed with regard to what to expect during your assessment and more prepared to face the tasks presented to you on the day. I hope to enhance your knowledge and give you examples to allow you to practise in a safe environment at home, which, in turn, should make you more confident during your assessment.

This book cannot replace practice and face-to-face feedback by others. Therefore, if you can, use the examples provided in this book to practise with friends and colleagues. Find someone you trust to give you honest and constructive feedback to allow you to improve.

I would highly recommend attending a formal course. Find a course with a small number of candidates that aims to give individual feedback related to your performance in the practical challenges you will face during your assessment. Look at who is teaching on the course. Are they trained? Have they experience of the application process?

If you do decide to attend a course, be honest with yourself and listen to the feedback given. It is very unlikely that the feedback you receive from a formally trained course tutor is inaccurate. Remember that they are trying to help you improve. They have nothing to gain from lying to you. If you are given feedback that you do not agree with, reflect on it for a while. Could it be true? I have lost count of the number of candidates who arrive at a course stating that one of their strengths is communication and, when it comes to showing those skills in a practical station such as role play, cannot accept any hints and tips on how to improve. If you believe you are the best at something, you may be right, but everyone has the capacity to improve. Why not aim to be even better? Choose a course that will give you the individual attention to achieve that.

Good luck!

Gail

About the Author

I have been where you are now. I have first-hand experience of the selection process and understand how you are feeling now in the run-up to the Stage 3 assessment. This insight, in addition to the following experience, puts me in a unique position to write this book. I hope you find it useful and wish you the best of luck!

My experience includes:

- Currently working in General Practice
- 10 years of clinical medical practice
- 14 years' experience of teaching others
- Formal training in all aspects of communication from non-verbal to specific verbal communication
- Professionally trained actress
- Work as an actor patient for medical examinations
- The use of role play and forum theatre to teach a variety of professionals (including civil servants, lawyers and medical personnel)
- Running one-day Stage 2/ Stage 3 courses for GPST applicants for ISC Medical

ISCMEDICAL
Interview Skills Consulting

The selection centre

The Stage 3 assessment for General Practice is undertaken at a selection centre. There are some variations over the country, but all are based on 3 separate, individually-marked stations. These stations are:

Station 1: Role play/ Simulated patient consultation

Station 2: Group discussion exercise

Station 3: Prioritisation/ written task

All three stations and their common variations will be discussed at length in the following chapters. They can be assessed in any order on the day so follow any instructions given to you closely.

It is highly unlikely that you will be assessed by formal interview, although those applying for academic General Practice should be aware that some deaneries have a separate interview process including a structured question and answer section. Your local deanery will tell you if there is a formal assessed interview and there are many books and courses that cover this type of interview. Preparation and practice is always the key.

Please read all the information sent to you (usually by email) by your individual deanery. Things change, so check your email daily.

ISCMEDICAL
Interview Skills Consulting

Set-up and practical advice

Timing

The majority of selection centres will run over a whole morning or afternoon, so don't be surprised if you are told to be at the assessment centre for 3 hours. If this is the case, the three assessed tasks are likely to last 20 minutes each, with breaks in between.

There are one or two centres that only allow 10 minutes per assessed task and run more like an OSCE (observed structured clinical examination) over 1 hour. The tasks are the same, but the set-up is different. In these centres, you will start your assessment as guided and, each time the bell rings, you will move on to your next task or to a rest station. Read the information sent to you so that you know which one applies to you.

Punctuality

Ensure that you turn up on-time. If the centre is in an area that you don't know well, plan your route in advance. Try the route beforehand so you know how long it will take you. Allow some extra time for unexpected delays. It sounds obvious, but how many times have you seen candidates rushing in at the last minute, out of breath and stressed? Don't let this be you. Your chance of getting a job rests on this one half-day. Why risk it?

Organisation

The selection centres run to a tight timetable. In addition to turning up on-time, it is important that you know where you need to be and at what time within your centre. When you arrive, you may be given a paper copy of a timetable; or it may be on a board or overhead projector (OHP) as you enter. Make a note of your candidate number and work out which room you should be in and at what time each station will start. Be punctual. Be prepared. Take with you a pen and some paper to write down the timetable just in case you are not given a hard copy of it.

What will happen on the day?

After signing in, you will probably be given a candidate number and asked to wear this on a badge or sticker for the duration of the assessment. Many

centres then take your photograph to ensure that the correct person is attending each part of the assessment. There will then be a waiting area for all the candidates to gather in prior to the start of the assessment.

What to wear

Read the information sent to you. Most selection centres state that you should be smart, but casual. What does that mean? Be comfortable, but remember that you are being assessed for a professional job and that one of the assessments is with a simulated patient. You need to look presentable enough to meet a "patient" (who may be a traditional older patient), but comfortable enough to sit for 2-3 hours. There are people who wear suits but many are dressed in their usual (possibly best) work clothes. If you are buying something new, try it on and wear it at home for a few hours. You need to ensure that nothing disrupts your concentration for the time that you are there. The tight shirt, hot or itchy jacket, skirt that needs pulling down or top that rides up to show your midriff are all distractions that are easily avoided.

Ladies, it doesn't matter if you wear a skirt, dress or trousers as long as it fits the above criteria. Be comfortable and professional.

As an actor, I never feel fully in character until I put on the shoes to complete the costume. It is the same for me in interviews. Think about your footwear. Make sure your shoes are comfortable. If they are new, wear them for a while at home. Avoid the distracting blister that is bound to happen on the day. If they are old, make sure they are cleaned. There may not be an explicit mark for the way you dress but it will make you look more credible and professional; it will also give you that added bit of confidence you need to spur you on.

Attitude

You are unlikely to be marked for the way in which you behave outside of the three structured assessed tasks, but in theory there is someone watching you from the minute you enter the selection centre until the moment that you leave. Think about the way in which you wish to be perceived. It does not mean that you should take on a character as you enter the building; one of the strengths of the assessment centre is that it assesses each candidate over a long period of time and so, unless you are a fabulous actor, it is unlikely that you will be able to maintain a false personality over a prolonged period of time. Instead, be yourself, but show the side of your personality that you want others to see. The staff who greet you and formally sign you in deserve as

much respect as the patient whom you will meet in the role-play / simulated patient consultation station. The other candidates are competitors, but they are also your colleagues and, as you will see later, your interaction with them will be formally assessed. You can start to build a relationship with your colleagues as soon as you sign in; I will comment more on this later. The last thing you need is to show disrespect towards another candidate who might end up in your own group discussion station later.

Official documentation to take with you

Read the information sent to you by your individual selection centre and follow that information. They often ask for the original and a photocopy of a number of official papers. If a copy is requested, ensure that you take it along. They will keep the photocopy once they have checked it alongside the original.

Avoid leaving any original document behind. It is very common for these to go missing. If it is essential that you leave an original document, ensure you have a photocopy at home and get a receipt from the member of staff who is taking it away. This way, if the original is not returned to you, you have proof that it was handed over to an official. Ensure that you take their name so that you can claim any reimbursement required for originals to be replaced.

The evidence commonly expected includes:

1 – Photographic identification
    This is required to prove you are who you say you are. Your NHS card or passport is normally sufficient.

2 – Driving licence
    One of the eligibility criteria for entry into General Practice training is that you have a valid driving licence or can demonstrate that you can fulfil the requirements of the post (e.g. providing emergency care, home visits). You may be forgiven for thinking that, since most of you will start training in a hospital, you do not need a driving licence straight away; however, many GPST rotations will have an ITP (innovative training post) in the first two years, which will mean working in General Practice before year three. If you do not have a valid driving licence, do not panic. Write a letter stating that you are willing to provide your own transport when required. This may mean paying for taxis or purchasing a bicycle while learning to drive, but this declaration will be enough to satisfy the entry criteria.

3 – Evidence of qualifications

Your primary medical qualification (translated into English if not originally in English) and any postgraduate examinations certificates that you have attained.

4 – Evidence of competencies

Foundation doctors will need to take along their signed certificate stating that they have achieved Foundation Year 1 (FY1) competencies, and if possible Foundation Year 2 (FY2) competencies. If you have not achieved FY2 competencies, get a letter from your current educational supervisor stating that they expect you to have achieved the required competencies by the end of your FY2 year.

Non-foundation doctors, which include those applying for shortened schemes, those trained in the old PRHO/SHO system, and those who trained abroad, will need to take the equivalent evidence for the level to which they are applying.

If applying to GPST1: take evidence of completion of your "house officer" year of training. It is probably worth getting a letter from your current educational supervisor stating that you have achieved the equivalent of the FY1 and FY2 competencies. A list of these competencies can be found on the internet for clarification.

If applying to GPST2/GPST3: as for GPST1, but you also need evidence proving that you have completed the additional training to enter at a higher level. To ensure that you will have the required experience by the end of your GP training, you should contact the GP Certification Unit, which is part of the Royal College of General Practitioners (RCGP). They will ask you to send in your curriculum vitae (CV) for assessment and will give you a letter stating a provisional estimate of the amount of further training that you require to become a GP. Take this letter to your selection centre.

You will also need evidence that each post you have completed and you wish to count towards General Practice has been approved for General Practice training and signed off. A VTR2 form is the current method of approval. These forms can be found on the RCGP website. You will need the educational supervisor for each post to sign the form, get a formal hospital stamp added, and then send the form (keeping a photocopy at home) to the department of General Practice in the deanery where the

post was undertaken for a formal signature of approval. This form will then be returned to you. Take it to your selection centre.

If your experience does not fit into the usual pattern, or if some of the jobs you are trying to get approved are outside of the United Kingdom (UK), or your approved jobs added to your additional training are over seven years in total, then you will also need advice from the Postgraduate Medical Education and Training Board (PMETB). If this applies to you, the route of your application for your Certificate of Completion of Training (CCT) at the end of your training programme will be slightly different than those progressing through a three-year training programme (ST1-ST3). Don't worry too much about this now, but be aware of it for the future.

5 – Portfolio and CV

Currently, there is no requirement to take along your CV and portfolio (many of which will be internet-based in the future) to your assessment centre, unless your individual centre requests to see it. You may not receive the information from the selection centre until a few days before you go, so it is good practice to have an up-to-date CV and ensure that your portfolio is completed well in advance of the Stage 3 assessment. Specialties other than General Practice often have a section of their interview dedicated to reviewing the evidence candidates they bring along. This is not the case currently with General Practice, but, as ever, things change, so be prepared for every eventuality.

Job selection

You are often asked to rank the available rotations within your deanery at the selection centre. Some deaneries will give you the information in advance by post or email and give you time at home to think about your preferences for where you would like to work. Others present you with a list of regions or individual rotations when you arrive for you to rank in order of preference. Make sure you have thought about this before you go. Go onto the deanery website and look through the rotations. Think about the geography and, if you don't know the area, buy and take along a map to your assessment. Don't be caught out or risk the added pressure by being presented with this on the day. A couple of hours of advance planning go a long, long way.

Additional tasks

Some deaneries will give you an introductory talk at the beginning of your selection centre to explain the process. Many will have a question and answer section at some point during the session. There are some deaneries that state that they have an "unmarked, structured interview" in addition to the 3 assessed tasks. This, as the title states, is not marked, but gives you time to ask questions, state your preferences for places to work and allows the deanery to get feedback from you. Again, make sure that you read the information sent to you.

The final request at the selection centre is usually for feedback if this has not been covered in a question and answer session or "unmarked, structured interview". Those organising the selection centre take the feedback you give seriously and your comments will shape the selection centres of the future. Please spend a little time giving honest feedback. Your voice and opinion are important.

Assessment Criteria

Having completed the Stage 1 eligibility application form and passed the Stage 2 exam-based assessment, it is now assumed that you have the clinical knowledge and that you fulfil the criteria required to achieve a place on a GP training scheme. Stage 3 is a way of choosing the best candidates by assessing the core competencies and shortlisting criteria as determined nationally.

GPST Person Specification

The National Person Specification for General Practice training is published by the National Recruitment Office for General Practice Training (see http://www.gprecruitment.org.uk/vacancies/specification.htm).

The main competencies that will be tested at the selection centre include:

- Empathy & Sensitivity
- Communication Skills
- Conceptual Thinking & Problem Solving
- Coping with Pressure
- Organisation & Planning
- Managing Others & Team Involvement
- Professional Integrity
- Learning & Personal Development

Read carefully through the specification, digest it and appreciate the qualities that the assessors will be looking for. Each of the tasks will be testing two or three of the core competencies. The basic principles of each of the core competencies are also explained in detail in the General Medical Council (GMC) publication entitled *Good Medical Practice* (2006). Make sure that you read your booklet attentively. If it has been accidentally filed in the bin, you can find it on the GMC website at www.gmc-uk.org.

Example of competencies assessed by each task

The simulated patient / role play
This will clearly test your communication skills, your empathy and sensitivity and, to some degree, your clinical knowledge base. Depending on the

scenario it may also test your professional integrity, probity and your ability to cope with pressure.

Group exercise
This will be testing your communication skills, your ability to work in a team, and your ability to problem solve and work under pressure. It may also (task dependent) test your organisational skills, professional integrity and probity.

Prioritisation exercise
This is definitely testing your ability to solve problems, work under pressure and your personal organisation. As you will see later, it is also possibly testing your multidisciplinary teamworking skills.

There is a large element of crossover between the tasks. Be aware of all the possible elements of assessment for each task. The more you prepare, the more likely you are to perform and score well on the day.

Introduction & Techniques

One of the three tasks that you will be expected to complete is the simulated patient or role-play exercise. Imagine that this is a real outpatient clinic or a real GP surgery. Imagine that the "actor patient" is a real patient and you will perform much better. The moment people start to think about "acting", things tend to fall apart. This task is not designed to catch you out or make you feel embarrassed. It is there to see how *you the doctor* behave when you are with real patients. Be yourself, but "play the game".

Playing the game

Those of you who have completed your driving test will know that there are things you do in your test to make sure that the examiner sees you doing them. This is what I mean by "playing the game". In your driving test, you turn your whole head to look in the rear-view mirror, while, in everyday driving, most of us just move our eyes. The role play is exactly the same. You need to make sure that the assessors see you performing certain tasks. To enable them to see you doing this, you need to show them very clearly what you are doing and thinking during the exercise. It is not enough to assume that they have picked up on things.

In an ideal world there would be real patients for this assessment. The only way to standardise the task is to put actors in their place but you need to treat the actors as you would your own patients.

Make it real

Having worked as an actor patient, I can assure you that, as long as your selection centre is using a reputable company to supply the actors, they are highly skilled, formally trained and very experienced at the roles that they are expected to perform on the day. They want to help you and will do everything they can to make sure that you are on the correct path; but they cannot put words in your mouth and, if you do not pick up on the clues that they throw at you, they will get stuck. If you do not ask them the right questions, it is almost impossible for them to help you gain those all-important ticks in the boxes that will score you points. This is where this book and good-quality courses will help you. I cannot tell you what to say as the exact questions and phrases will be very much dependent on the type of situation and patient that you get; but if you know what the assessors are looking for and you have a framework in

mind, then you are much more likely to ask the right sort of questions and succeed.

Listen

The most important piece of advice I can give you for this exercise, and indeed for your clinical practice as a whole, is LISTEN. Patients (and actor patients) tell us everything we need to know. Not necessarily in the order that we would want, and not always in an easily identifiable way, but listen, listen, listen. When you go back to work, practise with your own "real" patients. Try not saying anything; try using silence; try nodding and acknowledging instead of telling them what is about to happen. Put the patient in the driving seat and see what magical information you receive. Even the patient who sits in silence is telling us something. Do we intimidate them? Are they frightened? Are they listening? Are they trying to work out what to say to you? Are they trying to phrase a question but don't know how to ask? Give them space and see what happens.

Silence

In 1967, the Tremeloes sang a song called "Silence is Golden", and it definitely holds in modern medical practice. I am not suggesting that you sit in silence with your actor patient for 5 minutes, but often "less is more". The less you say in the opening minutes of the consultation, the more information you will get from the patient and that golden information may just point you in the right direction to score well. Try practicing it at work. Greet your patient and ask them how you can help. Then let them talk for a couple of minutes before you interrupt. See what else you find out. These skills are not just important for the role-play assessment; they will also improve your clinical skills and patient interaction. Try it.

In the role play, the actor giving you a clue as to what they want to talk about often fills the silence. This is where the listening can be crucial. Listen to every word they say. If they are repeating the same phrase time and time again, it is often because it is a clue; if you follow it up, it will unlock another part of the consultation that will gain you extra marks.

What will happen?
Once again, read the information sent to you from your selection centre for definitive clarification. Most centres will give you 20 minutes to complete the

role play though a few may only have 10 minutes, if based on the OSCE set-up. The principles are the same.

Inside the consultation room with you will be one or two assessors. They will be GP examiners or educational psychologists who are trained to mark you on the strict criteria of the selection centre. Be polite when you enter the room, but ignore them. They are there to mark you, not to help, guide or advise you. Do not worry about them being able to see everything. If they can't see you, they will move. Try to forget that they are present. You may hear them writing throughout your entire assessment; try to ignore it.

Read the brief

You will be given 5 minutes to read the doctor's brief before the patient comes in. Read it, read it and read it again. This is just like a referral letter or a handover from another doctor.

It may be something very vague such as:

Mrs Ben, aged 35, has come to see you for the results of her test. All bloods and X-rays are normal.

It may also be something fairly complicated:

Mrs Ben, aged 35, has come to see for the fourth time complaining of the same symptoms: sleepless nights and cough. She has never coughed up blood and has no sputum production. You have fully examined her every time you have seen her in the past and sent her for numerous investigations including a chest X-ray and routine bloods. All investigations are normal.

Take your time and read the information. Time after time, I see candidates making assumptions, adding information to that given or ignoring the information given in the brief. If the information is not there, do not assume anything. What would you do in real life? You would check the notes and, if you can't find them, then you would ask the patient. The role play is no different to your real practice. The information given to you is accurate. If it says that the investigations are normal, that is what it means. Do not assume they have been reported wrongly. Do what you would do in real life. If it says

that you have examined her in the past then that is what you have done. Believe what is written down.

Set up the room

Use the 5 minutes that you are given to set up the consultation room as you wish. There may be points given for "setting up a safe environment". This doesn't mean taking a can of paint and redecorating the walls, but it does mean moving the furniture to a comfortable position, i.e. one that is suitable for consulting in.

When you arrive, the chairs may be either side of a desk (Figure 1). If this is not comfortable for you, move them. I am often asked for the ideal set-up and the ideal distance between chairs. There is no right answer to this. You need to be able to see your patient and the patient needs to be able to see you. You must be close enough to touch the patient (or to hand them some tissues) if required, but not so close that you intimidate them or are touching knees. Practise at work. Try the chairs in different positions. Try different distances. Try with and without a desk. You will rapidly become aware of what is comfortable for you and for the patient. If you find your patients moving their chairs backwards during a consultation then you are probably too close. If you feel that you need to move your chair forward then it is likely that you are positioned too far away.

Figure 1. Poor positioning of chairs. The table is a barrier between the doctor and the patient

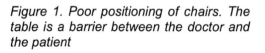
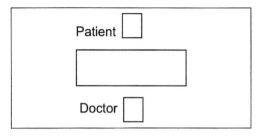

Figure 2. Suggested alternative set-ups. The desk is no longer a barrier. Work out your own preferred distance between the patient and doctor chairs. See what feels comfortable. Try without a desk if that is more comfortable for you.

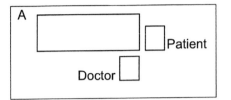

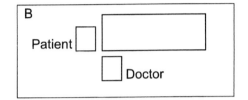

Assessment criteria / marking scheme

The role-play station is designed to test your communication skills, your empathy and sensitivity and, to some degree, your clinical knowledge base. Depending on the scenario, it may also be used to assess your professional integrity, probity and your ability to cope with pressure.

The marking schemes vary from year to year and sometimes also from deanery to deanery. However, there are some common themes that are likely to feature prominently. These would include:

1 – Creating a safe environment

As mentioned above, use your 5 minutes of preparation time to set the room up to ensure an adequate "safe" consultation can be performed.

2 – Introduction and putting the patient at ease

If you are given the patient's name, use it. Call the patient into the room by going to the door to greet them. Shake hands if this is natural for you and guide them to their seat. It has been known for an actor patient who is not guided by the candidate to sit in the "doctor's" chair. This can easily be avoided by guiding them.

3 – Active listening and encouragement

Remember: "Silence is golden". Start the consultation with an open-ended question. Give the patient the opportunity to speak so that you get threads that you can explore during the consultation.

- *How can I help today?*
- *What would you like to talk about?*
- *How are you?*

Choose a phrase that you would normally use to make it as natural as possible. Once you have done this, allow the patient time to speak, with a little silence if possible. Avoid using closed questions that push the patient towards "yes" or "no" answers, such as:

- *Have you come to see me again about your cough?*
- *You want to talk to me about your son, is that right?*

Active listening involves making full use of many of your senses:

- *Listen* to what they are saying – and to what they are not saying.
- *Look* and see how they are behaving. What is their body language saying?
- *Feel* the emotions that the patient is emitting and the emotions that they are evoking in you. Are they depressed, angry, nervous or agitated?

By opening in this way you have the added benefit of allowing yourself to settle into the consultation, and for your heart rate to begin to slow down.

Encourage the patient with prompts and by reflecting on their own words.

- *You said you are worried about ...*
- *Tell me more about ...*
- *What happened then?*

This will hopefully enable you to get a real sense of what the patient wants and thinks. The actor will try to give you as many clues as they can during this opening stage, so LISTEN to every word that they say.

4 – Relevant psychosocial information

This is the aspect of the consultation that is most often neglected by candidates and it is an area where it is very easy to score extra points. All patients are affected not only by their physical illness, but also by their psychological, financial, social and spiritual states. By incorporating these

in your consultation, you will gain a better understanding of the whole patient.

<u>Psychological</u>
- *How are you coping?*
- *How is this affecting you?*
- *How are you sleeping?*

<u>Financial</u>
- *Are you still managing to go to work?*
- *How do you afford to pay for your 8 pints of beer per night?*
- *Have you applied for any benefits or help?*

<u>Social</u>
- *Who is at home with you?*
- *Is there anyone you want me to call?*
- *What do you do in an evening?*
- *Do you have anyone to talk to?*

<u>Spiritual</u>
- *Who do you confide in?*
- *Do you have a Minister/ Rabbi/ Elder/ Priest you can talk to?*
- *Do you visit a Temple/ Church/ Mosque for support?*

Each individual patient and each individual scenario will lend itself to different psychosocial questions, but it is important to cover some aspect of it during your role play. Don't throw easy marks away.

Practise on your patients when you go back to work. Once you learn to incorporate these types of questions into your history-taking, it is amazing how natural they become and how much more relevant information you acquire about your patient.

5 – Expectations of the patient including any hidden agenda

Patients often attend wanting something or with an expectation. How many of you have been to visit your own GP and sat in the waiting room, planning not only what you want to say but also how you are going to say it? Our patients do exactly the same thing. A simple way of finding out if there is an expectation is by asking questions such as:

- *What were you expecting today?*
- *How do you want me to help you today?*
- *Is there anything else I can help you with today?*

These simple questions often open doors to hidden information. Try them out in your day-to-day work. See how often there is "something else" that you may otherwise have missed.

6 – Clinical questioning

You need to make sure that you have covered all the relevant questions relating to the presenting complaint.

In the case of lower back pain, are there any warning signs? Are the bowel and bladder intact? Is there any weakness?

For a persistent cough, has there been any haemoptysis or weight loss? Do not spend the whole scenario on this section. It is often the area that we are most comfortable in, but only a small number of marks will be given. Cover the essential points and move on.

7 – Explanation and differential diagnosis

Having spent time observing and talking to your actor patient, you will have an indication of their level of understanding. Having elicited their psychosocial history, you may have found out what their occupation is (assuming the brief hadn't given you the information anyway). You need to match your explanation of the differential diagnosis to their level of understanding. You will clearly use different words when talking to a Consultant physician than you would if the patient had learning difficulties. Pitch your explanation to the level of the patient. Using medical words is acceptable as long as the patient knows what they mean. You need to demonstrate that the patient understands (another tip for "playing the game"). It is not enough to assume that they do.

- *Do you know what I mean by "viral infection"?*
- *What do you understand when I use the word "cancer"?*
- *Is there anything you don't understand or want to ask me about?*

These are all ways of showing the assessor that you are checking that the patient understands, and another way to score easy points.

8 – Working diagnosis and management plan

It is obviously important to have an idea of a diagnosis and explain a clear management plan; but again there will only be a small number of points for this comfortable area of the consultation (this is what the MCQs and EMQs are for). If you know what is wrong with the patient, say it and propose a management plan. If, on the other hand, you have no idea what the diagnosis or problem is, then don't panic. Be honest and do what you would do in real-life situations. You would ask a colleague or your boss. You would do further tests or review them again.

- *I am not sure exactly what is causing your symptoms and so I would like to do some more tests / ask a colleague of mine to see you / see you again in a few days to review things.*

Remember to make the consultation as real as you can. Imagine this is a real outpatient clinic and behave the way you would do every day.

9 – Patient choice

If patients have a choice in what is about to happen, they are often more compliant with treatment and management plans. Offer the patient a choice.

- *We can either just wait and see what happens, or I could order a chest X-ray today.*
- *Most of the time this would settle without antibiotics. How do you feel about not having a prescription today?*
- *What would you like to happen now?*

Once again, try this in your everyday practice. Patients like to be involved. You will obviously meet patients that defer all decisions to the doctor but you are still allowing them a choice, even if that choice is for the doctor to decide.

10 – Checking the patient's understanding

It is important to confirm that the patient understands what has happened in the consultation and this is another way of "playing the game". Do not assume that the assessor has given you the point unless you have specifically asked the patient.

- *Do you understand?*
- *Is there anything that you didn't understand?*

Some people prefer to check the understanding by asking them to repeat part of the consultation.

- *Can I just check what you understood when I talked about diabetes?*
- *Just so I'm sure: can I ask you to talk me through the medication? How often should you take it? When will you take it?*

11 – Follow-up and review as required

We are now coming to the end of the consultation and it is important that the patient knows what is going to happen next. Let them know when to come back to see you.

- *Once your tests are all completed, call and make an appointment for a week later.*
- *If things don't settle down in 3-4 days, please come back and see me.*
- *If you get worse over the weekend or if you develop a rash that doesn't go away, please go straight to Accident and Emergency.*

By adding this kind of comment to the end of a consultation, you are adding an additional safety barrier for the patient.

12 – Actor patient's general impression

When working as an actor patient I am often asked for my opinion of the candidate. There may be a mark to be gained here if the patient felt you were clear, honest and trustworthy. The most common question I was asked as an actor patient was: *Would you come back and see this doctor?*

It is very easy to say "yes" and give the candidate the point if they followed the above advice. Even if the candidate did not know the diagnosis, as long as they offered follow-up, advice from others and practised safe medicine, I would always score them well. It was just as easy to withhold the point for the high-flying academic doctor who knew a hundred different causes for my symptoms but did not communicate clearly or put me at ease. The ideal would be to know the medicine and

communicate well but, on balance, I know out of the two which type of doctor I would rather be, and which type I would rather see. You need to make those decisions for yourself but, for the purpose of the role play, concentrate on your style over and above your knowledge of weird and wonderful diseases.

13 – Body language and physical interaction

In some role plays there will be marks for maintaining eye contact and for having an approachable and non-threatening manner. This is often picked up on through your body language.

I do not advocate that everyone should sit in the same way with an open body language, as suggested on some courses, but I do suggest that over the days and weeks before your assessment you start to think about what you do with your body during a consultation. Many of us have a habit that we are unaware of such as eating / sucking on hair, scratching or jiggling legs and feet. None of these make you a bad doctor, none will stop you getting a job; but they can be irritating for the patient and for the assessor. Why allow something that is easy to control to distract the assessor from your fantastic consultation style?

Start watching other people as they consult, in the canteen, at home or on television. Once you become aware of other people's habits you will see how annoying they can become.

Eye contact plays a crucial role in developing a rapport with the patient. Maintaining eye contact does not mean staring unblinking into your patient's eyes throughout the whole consultation, but simply ensuring that you maintain a good rapport. Also, through eye contact, you will gain important information about the patient and their emotions.

You would be amazed how many people spend the majority of a consultation looking at the carpet, the desk or up at the ceiling. We all think in different directions. I am a ceiling thinker, by which I mean that, when I'm under pressure and searching for an answer, my eyes drift upwards, looking for inspiration. This is acceptable for brief periods, but please be conscious of where you look and bring your focus back to the patient. It's easy once you become aware.

Start to think about your own and become aware of others' eye contact. You will soon realise what is comfortable, where you look for inspiration and what you need to do to improve things. Don't be put off if, for the first few days, you feel overly conscious, are unable to maintain eye contact or become fidgety. Persevere, work through the initial awkward phase and trust that with time it will become second nature and part of your natural consultation style.

14 – Remaining calm under pressure

I've added this, not because there will be an explicit mark for it, but because it is a very easy way to lose points. If you are given a difficult consultation and you feel irritated, if the patient becomes angry or is not listening to you, you may feel tempted to show your true feelings. If you start to feel irritated or annoyed, those emotions will be detectable to the patient and to the assessor. Recognise them early and take a deep breath. Pause and give yourself time to calm down. A good way of getting out of a sticky situation is to reflect the emotion back to the patient.

- *I see you are really angry about this.*
- *I'm sorry you feel so annoyed about this.*
- *What can I do to stop you feeling so angry about this?*

Such comments will hopefully encourage the patient to talk for a little longer giving you even more time to compose yourself, calm down and think of another approach. Try it, practise and work out which phrases work for you. Use your own words. Make it part of your everyday consultation style.

I am sure that, after reading this, you are beginning to realise how much is involved in scoring well in the role-play section. You may not be assessed on every individual point above, but if you make sure that you have covered everything you are certain to do well. When you practise role-play with colleagues and during the assessment, make sure that you address all those points as much as possible.

Clinical examination

There are usually no marks for clinical examination. Unless specifically told by your selection centre, there is no need to take along examination equipment. The emphasis on clinical diagnosis and management is small. You have already been assessed at Stage 2 on your clinical knowledge. This task is more about your consultation style rather than testing your ability to diagnose an unheard-of syndrome. In General Practice, if it looks like a dog and barks like a dog, it is probably a dog. It is unlikely to be a rare pink-spotted zebra that just happens to be wearing a dog-style coat with a hoarse voice and barking cough!

If you feel, for completeness, that you would like to examine the patient, please mention it – there may be a point to be scored. Use this as an example of "playing the game":

- *I would like to examine you, but will do so once we have finished here and I can take you next door to the examination room.*
- *I think it is important that we listen to your chest again. If it's all right with you I'll do this once we've finished talking before you go home.*

Whatever you decide to do, please don't approach the actor patient with arms outstretched ready to pull their clothes off. It is very frightening for the actor and, apart from anything else, they're not being paid enough to perform topless!

Communicating in different ways

I cannot emphasise enough times how important it is to treat this role play as though it were a real clinical situation and remember what you normally do in your own clinics and wards.

For some reason people forget that there are other ways of communicating in a role play when, in actual fact, they use these skills every day at work. Don't forget the use of a pen and piece of paper; these are usually supplied on the desk. To confirm a patient's understanding, we often write things down and draw pictures. If you feel this would help your role play, do it. If it is something you do every day, do it anyway. Don't change your consultation style for the assessment; instead, bring in all the positive things that you do every day to show how good you are. If you get stuck in a consultation, checking the

patient's understanding is also a good way to buy some time so that you can work out what you are going to say and do next. Try it.

The use of patient leaflets is also something that you can bring into your consultation. I'm not suggesting that you bring them along with you, but if you think it would enhance your role play to suggest a patient leaflet do so.

- *I think we have a leaflet on this at reception. Once we've finished I will go and find it for you.*
- *What I'd like to do is give you a leaflet on this for you to read at home. Why don't you come back once you've read it and we can talk again?*

If there are other things that you normally do during your consultations then do them. Use your own style and use your own words. Don't try to regurgitate word for word what is written in this book or what you are told on a course. Try things out and make them your own. Use this assessment preparation as a way of improving your day-to-day consultation style rather than a one-off change in your style for the purpose of getting a job.

How to end

You need to be aware of your own time. By all means, ask the assessor when you enter the room if they will give you a sign when there are 5 minutes or 2 minutes to go. If you are in the OSCE-type 10-minute consultation, there is usually a bell to tell you when to stop and move to the next station. You may simply be told "thank you", and asked to leave the room. It is better to be able to draw the consultation to a natural close by being aware of the time yourself.

Take along a desk clock or watch to put on the table so that you can see how much time you have left. Place it where you can see it easily without disrupting the consultation. Try not to spend time breaking eye contact just to look at the clock, particularly if it is at a sensitive part of the consultation.

If you finish early it doesn't matter as long as you feel that you have covered everything. However, if you have finished after 5 minutes then you are probably missing something. Go back to the psychosocial history and try to tease out any hidden agenda that the patient may have.

If you are happy that you have covered everything, end the consultation as you would normally do. Escort the patient to the door if it is comfortable to do so. Thank them for coming and reiterate your specified follow-up.

- *Thank you for coming. As I said earlier, call and make an appointment when you've had those tests done and I'll see you again.*
- *Is there anything else you would like to talk about today?*
- *Let me know how things go. If they don't improve, then please come back.*

Hidden agenda

This refers to something that the patient wants to talk about but doesn't introduce as their initial presenting complaint. You often have to dig a little deeper to find out what their true worries are. For example, the person who presents with a cough may have lost their father to lung cancer a few years previously and might be worried that they have cancer. If you don't ask about "any other worries" or about their psychosocial history then you may miss the whole reason for the consultation. Giving antibiotics to this patient will not resolve the underlying anxiety, and may not cure the cough.

Scare stories

We have all heard many scare stories about simulated patient/ role-play scenarios. Try to block these from your mind. The actor patients are trying to help you; the assessors want you to do well. The actor patient may try to push you to see how you react, but no one is trying to make you fail or make you look silly. If you feel that things are running away with you, take a deep breath and try to get back on track. Be honest with your actor patient.

- *I'm sorry, we seem to be going round in circles. Can I recap what we've said so far?*
- *I'm not sure we are communicating very well here, would you mind telling me what you've understood so far?*

Although a little staged, these types of phrases will buy you a little time to get back on the right track.

All the other scare stories are avoidable if you consult well. I was recently told of a case where an actor patient stormed out of the room in the middle of a scenario, angry and crying. The doctor was appalled. Surely this wasn't fair? By running the scenario again it became very clear that the doctor had antagonised the actor patient to such a degree that they responded in the way a real patient would. By rerunning the scenario using phases similar to those above, the patient was allowed to express his concerns and was given time

34

and space to understand the difficult diagnosis being expressed. By going at the pace and level of understanding of the patient, he was unable to become angry. Any signs of anger were acknowledged and explored further.

The actor patient will behave as a real patient. You must treat them as though they were a real patient.

How to prepare for the day

Practise; practise; practise. You can start right now by introducing all of the above principles into your own clinical consultations at work. Try a different approach each day and see what phrases work for you. Keep practicing and don't be put off if it feels unnatural for the first few days. Do you remember when you first learnt to take a history as a medical student? That too felt odd, didn't it? How does it feel now that you have had years of practicing the same thing every day? Normal? Well, that is exactly how you will feel with this. Persevere and I promise that it will all fall into place.

Practicing the technique at work is only one step. Use the role-play examples in this book, get together with some colleagues that you trust and play them out. You are unlikely to improve if you just read through the examples though. No one can pass a driving test just by reading a book; you need to get in the driving seat and do it for real.

Try playing the different roles (doctor, patient) in the role-play examples so that you see each consultation from different points of view. Look at how others consult. It is amazing how much you learn about yourself by watching others.

Watch colleagues consulting at work. Who do respect and why? What is it that they do that makes you think so highly of them? Talk to your patients and ask them who they think the best doctor is. You will often find it is their own GP because they know and understand them. Often patients will prefer the junior ward doctors rather than the experienced senior Consultants because the juniors spend more time talking and explaining. Find a patient that you get on with and ask them what they think is important when they see a doctor. Use whatever you think is appropriate from all these sources to enhance your own practice.

Finally, the gold standard of practice is to find a reputable and well-respected course that will allow you to practise with trained observers/ tutors. Make sure

it has a focus on role play and has a small number of candidates. Listen to the feedback and learn from the other candidates on the course. See what works well and what doesn't. Use everything you can to improve yourself.

Figure 3. Summary of proposed assessment criteria for role play

1. Creating a safe environment
2. Introduction and putting the patient at ease
3. Active listening and encouragement
4. Relevant psychosocial information
5. Expectations of the patient including any hidden agenda
6. Clinical questioning
7. Explanation and differential diagnosis
8. Working diagnosis and management plan
9. Patient choice
10. Checking the patient's understanding
11. Follow-up and review as required
12. Actor patient's general impression
13. Body language and physical interaction
14. Remaining calm under pressure

Section 2

Role-play
Practice Scenarios

How to use this section

To prepare for the role-play station, there is no substitute for practice. In this section, you will find several examples of role plays, which you can use to practise with colleagues and friends.

You can of course simply read through the examples if you wish (you will certainly pick up some information), but you will gain a lot more by playing them out. Ideally, to do this effectively you will need three people: one playing the doctor, one playing the patient and one observer. If you can, choose 2 colleagues whom you trust and set aside some proper time so that you do not rush the exercise. Each role-play scenario should take approximately 30 minutes in total, though you may want to play them several times, taking on different roles or with a patient reacting in different ways, in which case you may want to allow a longer period of time.

Structure

Each of our practice role plays has three parts:

1 – The brief for the doctor
This text represents what you, as a doctor, know about the patient and the circumstances of the consultation. It contains information that will be of use to you during the consultation, though there could be occasional red herrings. It is similar to the information that you will be given as a candidate on the day of the assessment at the selection centre.

2 – The brief for the patient
This is similar to the information that your actor patient will get on the day. It will let the patient know a little about the history, their hidden agenda (if there is one), and the points that you as the doctor need to try to find out during the consultation (e.g. psychosocial). In order not to spoil your learning experience, you should ensure that the person playing the doctor has not read this text before the start of the simulated patient consultation.

3 – A discussion on points to raise during the consultation
For each role play, detailed explanations will be given. This section will follow the style of the *Summary of proposed assessment criteria for role play* (see p.36). It is designed to give you an idea of the themes and ideas that you should have discovered and to encourage you not to forget to ask

certain questions such as the psychosocial history. Bear in mind though that there are many ways in which a specific situation can be handled and therefore the suggested approaches and comments do not represent a definitive answer. As you practise, you may find that other points are raised within your group.

How to run a role play

Ideally, there should be three of you, though you can also achieve excellent results with two.

The doctor
One person should take on the role of the candidate (i.e. the doctor). This person should only read the brief for the doctor and nothing else. This way you will make the exercise as real as it can be and comparable to the assessment itself.

The actor patient
The second person should take on the role of the patient. This person should only read the brief for the patient. On the day of your assessment, the actor patient that enters the room is the age and sex that you see in front of you. The practice role plays in the book can be played as either a male or female. Be yourself and try to be as real as you can for your colleague.

I personally think that you can learn as much by being a patient as you can by playing the role of the doctor. Even if the colleagues with whom you are practicing are not attending the Stage 3 assessment centre, try playing the patient at least once. It will help you understand not only how difficult it can be to get the information over if the doctor does not ask you the right questions, but also how easy the consultation can become if the correct questions are asked and the right attitude is demonstrated.

Playing the role of the patient will also show you how real emotions can feel whilst in the role; this is how your actor patient feels. They will follow the emotions that are invoked in them during the consultation. If you make them feel angry, that anger will continue until you help dissipate it. If you create an environment in which they feel sad and can cry, this is what will happen.

The observer (preferred but optional)
The third person should be the observer. This person sits and watches the doctor, making notes of what happens during the role play in order to give

clear, objective and structured feedback to the candidate playing the role of the doctor. The observer is also the timekeeper. When you first start to practise, you may want to give a sign to state that there are only 5 minutes remaining. As you get nearer to the assessment day, leave it up to the candidate to manage their own time, but stop them once their allocated time is up as would happen on the day. You do not need to comment on the patient's performance. The feedback you give is purely for the candidate/ doctor.

Timing

To undertake effective preparation, you will need to spend approximately 30 minutes on each role play, the time being split as suggested below:

Figure 4. Suggested time for each role play

5 minutes	The candidate reads the brief
15 minutes	Play out the scenario
10 minutes	Feedback / Debrief

Notes:
- The actor patient may wish to spend a little more time than the candidate to read the brief in order to fully understand their role.

- Although many role plays will be 20 minutes' long I suggest that you train with a time limit of 15 minutes, in the knowledge that, on the day of the exam, with a fully trained actor, the consultation may take a little longer. Having a shorter time limit will also enable you to focus your thoughts. If you prefer, you may take the full 20 minutes for the role play.

- The 10-minute feedback session is an indication and you can take as long as you wish. Those who are dedicated may also want to rerun all or part of the role play in a different way once they have read our suggestions to approach the scenario, which would obviously lengthen the session.

Escape

If possible you should try to stay in your role, even if the situation becomes tricky. However, when you first start running the scenarios, you may want to agree on a sign to allow either the doctor or the patient to come out of the role

play if you have to. This could be something as simple as raising your hand. On the day, you will not be able to take "time out", so start to work out ways of coping with the difficulties that you encounter. As you get closer to the day of the assessment, do not allow yourself to come out of role. Wait until the debrief at the end to discuss the difficulties.

Feedback / debrief

After the role play is finished, it is important to complete the exercise by debriefing. I find that it is better to take it in turns with each of the three participants having time to talk. Try answering the following questions as a way to start your feedback.

1 – The doctor
- *Was it easy? Hard?*
- *What do you think went really well? Why did it go well?*
- *What do you think was difficult? Why?*
- *How did you feel during the role play?*
- *If this patient came in to see you in your real clinic tomorrow, how would you handle it?*

2 – The patient
- *Would you come back and see this doctor?*
- *How did the doctor make you feel?*
- *Did you have time to explain your concerns?*
- *Did the doctor get all the information that was on your sheet?*
- *Why did they get the amount of information that they did?*
- *What was good?*
- *What do you wish they had asked you?*
- *Did you understand everything?*
- *Did the doctor listen to what you were saying?*
- *Was there anything that you noticed that might have put you off or irritated you?*
- *Did the doctor have adequate eye contact with you?*

3 – The observer
- *How clear was the consultation?*
- *Did the doctor cover all the points in the summary of proposed assessment criteria for role play?*
- *Did the doctor get all the information that was on the patient sheet?*
- *Why did they get the amount of information that they did?*

- *What was good?*
- *What do you wish they had asked the patient?*
- *Did the patient appear to understand everything?*
- *Did the doctor listen to what the patient was saying?*
- *Was there anything that you noticed that might have put off or irritated you if you had played the patient?*
- *Did the doctor have adequate eye contact with the patient?*

These questions are just a guide as a way to start your feedback. As you practise, you will form your own style of feedback. When others feedback on your performance, treat each comment as a learning point. You may not agree with everything that your colleagues say, but it does not mean that there isn't an element of truth in their comment. On the day of the assessment, all that will matter is what the examiners and the actor patient will think, and not what *you* think.

Do not take the feedback that you receive as a negative criticism; instead, view it as an opportunity to reflect on your performance and to improve. If, however, you do not feel comfortable receiving feedback from those who are working with you then try working with other people, or try going to a course.

Above all, remember: if everyone is saying the same thing about your performance, then it is probably right.

Practice Role Play
Scenario 1

ROLE PLAY SCENARIO 1

Doctor's Brief

You are based in General Practice.

Mr/Mrs Edwards is coming to see you today for the third time this month, complaining of excessive tiredness. He/she is unable to complete his/her normal day-to-day activity without stopping for a nap at least once per day.

At his/her initial appointment, you examined the patient fully and took a detailed physical history to rule out a serious cause. You requested all routine blood tests including a full blood count and thyroid function tests.

At the second appointment you explained to the patient that the results for all the investigations performed were completely normal and that you could find no physical cause for the tiredness. You rechecked the history and examined him/her again. You suggested a "wait-and-watch approach", with reassurance.

He/she has returned today with exactly the same symptoms. There are no changes to the physical history, clinical examination or blood tests. You do not need to repeat these.

ISCMEDICAL
Interview Skills Consulting

Use this box to make your pre-consultation notes

ROLE PLAY SCENARIO 1

Patient's Brief (Mr/Mrs Edwards)

You are going to see your GP for the third time this month. You have a good relationship with them and like them a lot.

You initially presented because you were tired, run-down and needing to sleep in the middle of the day. Your GP has fully examined you twice and completed routine blood tests that have come back completely normal. On your second visit the doctor explained that all the test results were normal and suggested a "wait-and-see" approach.

You are still tired and needing to nap in the middle of the day.

Important history that your doctor does not yet know

You are not working at the moment and have chosen to stay at home to look after your three young children (aged 1, 3 and 4). Your partner works away and is spending more and more nights away from home. You are worried that they are having an affair. You are embarrassed to talk about this and will only do so if specifically asked about your home life and relationships.

If the doctor is compassionate and asks about your partner, open up and talk. Initially, refuse any help that is offered as a way of talking to your partner. If the doctor persists or offers alternatives, accept their help.

With your partner being away from home, you are up every night with your 4-year-old child who suffers from cystic fibrosis and is currently very unwell. You need some help at home but your extended family lives far away and you are worried that, if social services find out that you are not coping, they will take your children away from you. If the doctor mentions health visitors or social services, you should become very guarded and frightened about your children being taken away from you.

If the doctor is compassionate and allays your fears of the children being taken away, open up and accept the help.

46

ROLE PLAY SCENARIO 1

Discussion

The first thing to do is read the brief. Read it and read it again. Did you do that? Did you get halfway through and forget something, which meant that you had to refer back to the brief?

Next ask yourself: "What do I know from the brief?" You know that the symptom is tiredness and daytime napping. In this case, the brief also tells you that the physical history, examination and routine tests are all normal. It is very common in a scenario of this type to fall into the trap of taking the history again. The brief specifically tells you that this is not necessary.

Start to think about what could be causing the patient's problem. Don't make assumptions, but start to pinpoint areas from the *Summary of proposed assessment criteria for role play* (p.36) that could be relevant in this case. If you start to think of these before the patient comes in, then you are more likely to ask appropriate questions.

1 – Creating a safe environment

Did you move the furniture?
Were you sitting too close or too far away from the patient?
Was it comfortable?

2 – Introduction and putting the patient at ease

Did you use the patient's name? If not, why not? It was in the brief.
You may want to start the scenario by finding out what the patient remembers in order to ensure that your information matches theirs.

- *Hello again Mr/Mrs Edwards, it's nice to see you again. How can I help today?*
- *Can you remember what we talked about last time?*

By asking this kind of open questions, you will allow the patient to talk, which will allow you to find out exactly why they have come to see you. In this case, the patient wanted to talk about the psychosocial causes of their fatigue, but it may have been that the patient was unhappy with your previous treatments and investigation and wanted another test or referral to a specialist. Do not assume anything.

Do not add any information to the brief unless the patient tells you that information. Just like in real life, the only things we know about our patients are written down or told to us during a consultation. We don't make things up in the hospital/ clinic. Don't do it in the role play.

3 – Active listening and encouragement

Did you listen and give the patient time to talk?
Did you allow them to tell you why they were there?
If they were quiet, did you encourage them to talk using open questions?
Did you use any silence?

Did you listen, look and feel?

Did you listen to what they were saying?
Did you listen to what they were not saying?
Did you look and see how they behaved?
What was their body language saying?
Did you feel any emotions the patient gave out?
Did you feel any emotions evoked in you?
Were they depressed, angry, nervous or agitated?

4 – Relevant psychosocial information

This was the main focus for this scenario, but very easily missed if you did not ask the questions.

Look at the patient's brief.

The patient is given clear instructions not to talk about their worries over their partner unless specifically asked. If you have missed the "social" questions, you have missed the whole purpose of this scenario. See how easy it is to lose points? Equally, by asking a few simple questions, it is very easy to get all the information you need from the patient.

Psychological
- *How are you coping?*
- *How is it affecting you?*
- *How are you sleeping at night?*

Financial
- *Are you working at the moment?*

Social
- *Who is with you overnight to help?*
- *Do you have anyone to talk to?*
- *Who is around in the daytime to help?*

Spiritual
- *Who do you confide in?*

5 – Expectations of the patient including any hidden agenda

Did you ask what the patient wanted?

- *How do you think I can help you today?*
- *What are you worried about?*
- *Is there anything else you would like to talk about?*

6 – Clinical questioning

Many people will have headed straight for the safe area of history-taking and clinical questioning. Did you? The brief explicitly states that you do not need to retake a history. It is appropriate to double-check that the symptoms are the same but time wasted on a thorough clinical history will impair your ability to probe into more appropriate avenues.

- *Can I just check if anything has changed since we last met?*
- *How are your symptoms compared to last time we met?*

If the patient states that nothing has changed and your brief also states that nothing has changed, move on.

7 – Explanation and differential diagnosis

In this scenario you have already ruled out a clinical cause for their symptoms. You could have explained this again to the patient, making sure that you used words and terms that they would understand.

- *With all the tests and examinations we have done before, I can't find any physical cause for your symptoms.*
- *Do you remember that, last time, we talked about the fact that there was no evidence of a physical cause for your symptoms?*

The differential diagnosis does not really come into play in this scenario.

8 – Working diagnosis and management plan

If you managed to elicit the psychosocial information from the patient, then you will hopefully have decided that the working diagnosis is related to the patient's sick child, lack of sleep, poor support network, unsupportive partner and worries about his/her partner's affair.

As a management plan, there are several approaches:

a. *Support from you, the GP*
Follow-up appointments, offer of counselling or other help.

b. *Support from the health visitors for the 4 year old with cystic fibrosis*
All children under 5 years of age should be supported by a health visitor when required. If you mentioned this in the role play, the patient may have become very guarded (as per their brief), allowing you to explore their fears of removal of their children by social services. This is an unfounded fear and, as stated in the patient brief, if you were compassionate and allayed the fears of the children being taken away then the patient would have opened up to you and accepted your help. If this didn't happen, why didn't it? What happened to stop a positive resolution?

c. *Support from the family*
You could explore the option of extended family members or friends to help.

d. *Support from the partner*

Discussing with the patient the amount of support that they could expect from their partner may have allowed the issue of the partner's affair to surface. This in turn may have led to a discussion about how the patient's issues should be discussed with the partner and also about the possible involvement of external agencies and counselling services such as Relate.

9 – Patient choice

Did you ask the patient if they had any ideas about what they wanted?

- *Who would you like me to contact?*
- *What would you like us to do next?*

10 – Checking the patient's understanding

Did the patient understand? Did you ask? If not, why not? Remember it is not enough to assume they know what is happening. You need to *show* the assessors that you have asked.

11 – Follow-up and review as required

This is very important in this case. Your patient is not coping and has three young children. You need to ensure that the children are safe by involving the health visitor.

If you were compassionate, the patient would have agreed to this follow-up. If, for some reason, your patient refused to allow the health visitor to become involved, then ask yourself why.

The patient's brief was specific, so what happened to make them disagree? Whether they agreed or not, you do have a duty to inform the health visitor if you have any concerns about any child under the age of 5. For any serious concerns (not appropriate in this case), social services, the local paediatrician and the police can also assist.

12 – Actor patient's general impression

You have hopefully covered this in your feedback, but do you think the patient will come back and see you?

13 – Body language and physical interaction

How was your eye contact?
Are you a floor or ceiling thinker?
Do you think you were too close/ too far away from the patient?
Did you notice any irritating habits?

14 – Remaining calm under pressure

Were there any hairy moments?
Did the patient get upset or angry?
How did you respond to this?
Did you feel yourself becoming emotionally involved, angry or irritated?
What did you do to resolve it?
What would you do next time?

There is a lot of information in the discussion and you may not have time to cover all of it in your role play. The discussion is there to point out all possible approaches and information that you could get from the scenario. Try rerunning it to see if you can practise other ways of approaching the patient to glean as much information as you can. The more you try and practise, the easier and the more natural it will feel on the day.

Practice Role Play
Scenario 2

ROLE PLAY SCENARIO 2

Doctor's Brief

You are based in General Practice.

Mr/Miss Dewen who is newly registered at the practice comes to see you with lower back pain. He/she attended for the first ever time 2 weeks ago complaining of acute lumbar back pain following picking up some heavy shopping. At the time, there were no sinister red flag signs; his/her physical (including a full neurological) examination was normal. He/she was advised to continue his/her regular activities and was prescribed diclofenac (a non-steroidal anti-inflammatory drug – NSAID) three times a day in addition to over-the-counter paracetamol. He/she was signed off work as cabin crew for an international airline for 2 weeks.

He/she returns today with the same symptoms. The history and physical examination have not changed.

For your information a "red flag" sign is one that would alert you to serious underlying pathology causing spinal cord compression or cauda equina syndrome which, if not decompressed surgically (or, in the case of malignancy, with radiotherapy), can lead to permanent neurological sequelae. In the case of back pain, this would include rapid leg weakness, saddle anaesthesia and bowel / bladder symptoms.

ISCMEDICAL
Interview Skills Consulting

Use this box to make your pre-consultation notes

ROLE PLAY SCENARIO 2

Patient's Brief (Mr/Miss Dewen)

You are cabin crew for an international airline. You love your job, but you have just been moved from working in the first-class section of the airplane to the economy section. You feel that this is because your new line manager – who has been in the job for 2 months – has taken a dislike to you. You feel that you are being victimised at work and you are frightened that you will lose your job if you make a fuss and confront this manager.

Luckily, 2 weeks ago you pulled your back whilst picking up some heavy shopping and the doctor you saw at the time prescribed some pain killers and gave you a certificate for 2 weeks off work. These 2 weeks are now over and you are frightened to go back to work.

When the doctor initially asks you about your back trouble, tell them that it has not really improved and that you feel unable to go back to work.

In reality, nothing has really changed since the last appointment and it has not got worse. If anything, things are a little better, but you feel that more time off work will help your recovery. The real reason you want more time off work is that your new line manager will move teams in 4 weeks' time and if you are absent for that time you will not have to work in economy and face further bullying.

If the doctor asks about your work, initially be reticent about the truth but give them a hint that all is not well. If they persist, open up and tell them the truth. In reality, your back pain is much better and you really only want the time off work to avoid your new manager.

If the doctor offers solutions to help, insist that the only thing that will help is to avoid the manager and not go back to work; therefore the only help that they can give you is a certificate stating "back pain" for a further four weeks off work. If they persist and offer alternatives, compromise and accept their help.

ROLE PLAY SCENARIO 2

Discussion

The first thing to do is read the brief. Read it and read it again. Did you do that? Did you get halfway through and forget something and have to refer back to the brief?

Next ask yourself: "What do I know from the brief?" You know that the patient attended once with back pain with no significant cause for concern. You know that nothing has changed from the previous history and examination. It is common for us to fall into the trap of the history-taking and, although it is important to double-check the "red flag" signs, you should not spend a large proportion of your time on it as you will lose valuable time.

Start to think about what could be causing the patient's problem. Don't make assumptions, but start to pinpoint areas from the *Summary of proposed assessment criteria for role play* (p.36) that could be relevant in this case. If you start to think of these before the patient comes in, then you are more likely to ask appropriate questions.

1 – Creating a safe environment

Did you move the furniture?
Were you sitting too close or too far away from the patient?
Was it comfortable?

2 – Introduction and putting the patient at ease

Did you use the patient's name?
If not, why not? It was in the brief.
You may want to start the scenario by finding out what the patient remembers in order to ensure that your information matches theirs.

- *Hello again Mr/Miss Dewen, it's nice to see you again. How can I help today?*
- *Can you remember what we talked about last time?*

By asking this kind of open questions, you will allow the patient to talk, which will allow you to find out exactly why they have come to see you. In this case, the patient wanted to talk about the psychosocial causes of their back pain, but it may have been that the patient was unhappy with your previous treatments and investigation and wanted another test or referral to a specialist. Do not assume anything.

Do not add any information to the brief unless the patient tells you that information. Just like in real life, the only things we know about our patients are written down or told to us during a consultation. We don't make things up in the hospital/ clinic. Don't do it in the role play.

3 – Active listening and encouragement

Did you listen and give the patient time to talk?
Did you allow them to tell you why they were there?
If they were quiet, did you encourage them to talk using open questions?
Did you use any silence?

Did you listen, look and feel?

Did you listen to what they were saying?
Did you listen to what they were not saying?
Did you look and see how they behaved?
What was their body language saying?
Did you feel any emotions the patient gave out?
Did you feel any emotions evoked in you?
Were they depressed, angry, nervous or agitated?

4 – Relevant psychosocial information

This was the main focus for this scenario, but very easily missed if you did not ask the questions.

Look at the patient's brief.

The patient is given clear instructions not to tell the doctor about their work worries unless specifically asked. If you have missed the "social" questions, you have missed the whole purpose of this scenario. See how

easy it is to lose points? Equally, by asking a few simple questions, it is very easy to get all the information you need from the patient.

Psychological
- *How are you coping?*
- *How is it affecting you?*
- *How are you sleeping at night?*

Financial
- *You have been off work for 2 weeks. How are you coping?*

Social
- *What are you able to do for yourself?*
- *Do you feel able to go back to work?*

Spiritual
- *Who do you confide in?*

5 – Expectations of the patient, including any hidden agenda

Did you ask what the patient wanted?

- *How do you think I can help you today?*
- *What are you worried about?*
- *Is there anything else you would like to talk about?*

6 – Clinical questioning

Many people will have headed straight for the safe area of history-taking and clinical questioning. Did you? The brief explicitly states that you do not need to retake a history. It is appropriate to double-check that the symptoms are the same but time wasted on a thorough clinical history will impair your ability to probe into more appropriate avenues.

- *Can I just check if anything has changed since we last met?*
- *How are your symptoms compared to last time we met?*

In this type of case it is also worth checking that there are no red flag signs once again. If the patient states that nothing has changed and your brief also states that nothing has changed, move on.

In this case, things have slightly improved, so you can be further reassured that there is no significant physical problem. Did you ask yourself why the patient presented? If things are improving why did they want more time off work? If this happens in your role play, ask yourself: "What am I missing?"

If things aren't clear, always go straight back to the psychosocial history.

7 – Explanation and differential diagnosis

After only 2 weeks of pain, which is improving with no sinister signs, your only differential diagnosis is one of musculoskeletal pain. Did you explain this to the patient in a clear way at a level that they understood?

8 – Working diagnosis and management plan

If you managed to elicit the psychosocial information from the patient you will hopefully have decided that the working diagnosis is a stress-related one resulting from a new line manager at work who is "bullying" the patient. If you didn't elicit this, ask yourself why. What else could you have asked to find out?

With regard to the management, there are several approaches:

a. *Support from you, the GP, in talking through the issues*
   You can start this in your role play, but often you will need to suggest another appointment. This could be a double appointment.

b. *Support from work*
   Is there someone at work that the patient can talk to?
   Is there a union representative that the patient can approach?
   What about the occupational health department for support?
   Is there a work counsellor?

c. *Support from the family/ friends*
   Who can the patient talk to at home?
   What friends can the patient rely on?

d. *Support from the Citizens Advice Bureau (CAB)*
    This is a free and confidential service where the patient can get advice regarding a number of matters including employment law, financial support and divorce.

9 – Patient choice

Did you ask the patient if they had any ideas about what they wanted?

- *Who would you like me to contact?*
- *What would you like us to do next?*

In this case the patient simply wanted signing off work with a bad back for another month.

The MED3 certificate is the certificate that we sign as doctors and that patients give to their employers justifying their absence from work. It is a legal document and we need to put a diagnosis on the form. In this case, to sign a patient off work with back pain when this is resolving and they are physically fit for work would be making an untruthful statement.

You could compromise with the patient and give them one further week off work for the back problem to resolve completely and ask them to try to resolve the problem at work by talking to the firm.

An alternative would be to sign them off with a stress-related problem if you clinically thought that the patient was significantly affected, again on the understanding that they would approach their work and try to resolve the problem.

10 – Checking the patient's understanding

Did the patient understand? Did you ask? If not, why not? Remember it is not enough to assume they know what is happening. You need to *show* the assessors that you have asked.

11 – Follow-up and review as required

Whatever happened in your scenario, follow-up is important in this case. Review of a patient who is signed off work with a psychological problem

is advisable to ensure that some progress is being made. If you resolved the problem in your scenario, it is always worth suggesting they return if they need to at any time for further help. In this case, the offer of a double appointment at the next visit to continue your support would also be invaluable.

12 – Actor patient's general impression

You have hopefully covered this in your feedback, but do you think the patient will come back and see you?

13 – Body language and physical interaction

How was your eye contact?
Are you a floor or ceiling thinker?
Do you think you were too close/ too far away from the patient?
Did you notice any irritating habits?

14 – Remaining calm under pressure

Were there any hairy moments?
Did the patient get upset or angry?
How did you respond to this?
Did you feel yourself becoming emotionally involved, angry or irritated?
What did you do to resolve it?
What would you do next time?

There is a lot of information in the discussion and you may not have time to cover all of it in your role play. The discussion is there to point out all possible approaches and information that you could get from the scenario. Try rerunning it to see if you can practise other ways of approaching the patient to glean as much information as you can. The more you try and practise, the easier and the more natural it will feel on the day.

Practice Role Play
Scenario 3

ROLE PLAY SCENARIO 3

Doctor's Brief

You are based in General Practice. Mr/ Mrs Gregory, whose daughter came to see you 1 month ago, has come for a general appointment. You have never met him/her before.

Information that you already know from the daughter

The daughter (Ellen) came to see you 1 month ago, as she was worried about her periods. She had been amenorrhoeic for 6 months. There was no physical evidence of disease other than being underweight (BMI 17.5). She denied over-exercising or starvation/binging. On deeper questioning, there were multiple stressors in her life including multiple debts and a split from her husband, which necessitated her moving back in with her parents and sister, who she said was dying from leukaemia. The sister is not a patient at the practice.

After offering support and explaining to her that the periods were most likely related to being underweight with the associated psychological problems as a probable cause, you arranged some routine tests and had arranged to see her again 1 week later. She has not attended any of the planned follow-up appointments and has not had her blood tests taken.

Use this box to make your pre-consultation notes

ROLE PLAY SCENARIO 3

Patient's Brief (Mr/Mrs Gregory)

You are attending a new GP as you are desperate. It feels as though your whole life is falling apart. You are happily married and have two children.

Your youngest daughter (Ellen) recently moved back into the house after a split from her husband and has stopped eating. You believe that she is suffering from anorexia after watching a recent documentary on the television. She has lost weight and last week you found four different types of laxatives in her bag. She attends the gym every day and no longer eats with the family. You have confronted her and she denies that there is any problem.

You spoke to her estranged husband. He is also worried about her weight. He told you that she had recently been to see her GP but that he did not know what it was for.

You want information from the GP. You know that your daughter is a patient there and want to check if she has recently visited the practice, what was said and if she is getting any help with her weight/ anorexia problem.

If the doctor refuses to engage with you about your daughter and offers no alternative, become angry and, if no resolution is put forward, storm out of the room.

If the doctor tries to re-engage in conversation, listen and respond to any advice or help that they provide. Deep down, you know that the doctor cannot give you any information about Ellen, but you do not know what else to do. You feel that you are the only one who cares.

If the doctor does give you information about Ellen, keep pushing to see how much information you can get out of them.

You want help not only for Ellen, but also for yourself. Do not divulge this information until the GP asks you about your feelings. You are finding it really difficult to cope and you really need someone to help you through this and to

guide you. If the doctor does not offer any solutions then become upset and disengage from the consultation. Accept any help that is offered.

An ideal ending would be to have a follow-up appointment offered for yourself and some form of contact offered for your daughter. This could be a joint appointment if that is suggested.

Important side issue
You have another daughter (your eldest daughter Sarah), who was diagnosed with leukaemia. She has now completed her treatment and is in remission. At some point in the role play, the doctor might indicate that Sarah is actually dying of leukaemia. This is information that he will have obtained from your daughter Ellen and which is incorrect. If the GP mentions that Sarah is dying, then first accuse him of lying and then accuse him of withholding information from you (does he know something that you don't know?).

67

ROLE PLAY SCENARIO 3

Discussion

The first thing to do is read the brief. Read it and read it again. Did you do that? Did you get halfway through and forget something and have to refer back to the brief?

Next ask yourself: "What do I know from the brief"?

You know nothing about the patient in front of you, but you know a lot about her family set-up and, as it turns out, about the main reason for the consultation since you have previously seen their daughter. This raises a confidentiality issue as Ellen is entitled to complete confidentiality. You should not tell the parent anything about your consultation with Ellen, and some people would say that you should not even acknowledge that Ellen has visited the surgery to see you previously.

Start to think about why the patient is presenting. It may not be related to the additional information. Don't make assumptions but start to pinpoint areas from the *Summary of proposed assessment criteria for role play* (p.36) that could be relevant in this case. If you start to think of these before the patient comes in, you are more likely to ask the appropriate questions.

1 – Creating a safe environment

Did you move the furniture?
Were you sitting too close or too far away from the patient?
Was it comfortable?

2 – Introduction and putting the patient at ease

Did you use the patient's name?
If not, why not? It was in the brief.
You have never met this patient before and so starting the consultation with a general open question would be most appropriate.

- *Hello Mr/Mrs Gregory. How can I help?*
- *We've not met before, I'm Dr _____. What can I do for you today?*

By asking such open questions you are allowing the patient to talk, thereby helping to ensure that you find out exactly why they have come to see you. In this case, the parent is initially seeking information about his/her daughter's health and help for the daughter's anorexia.

As stated above, confidentiality is the key here and it is important that you explain to Mr/Mrs Gregory that you are unable to give them the information that they want. The manner in which you do this will significantly affect the way the scenario is played out by the actor patient. Go back and read the patient's brief again. If you do this part of the consultation well, the actor patient will continue to engage. If you are blunt or do not offer any other suggestions, then the actor patient is primed to make things difficult for you.

One way of dealing with this opening is by not initially refusing to give any information but continuing to ask more open questions.

- *You must be very worried.*
- *Let's start by working out how this is affecting you rather than concentrating on what Ellen has said.*
- *What are your biggest fears?*

Remember not to assume anything. Do not add any information to the brief unless the patient tells you that information. Just like in real life, the only things we know about our patients is written down or told to us during a consultation. We don't make things up in the hospital/ clinic. Don't do it in the role play.

This is particularly important in this scenario as the doctor's brief states that Ellen had said that her sister was dying from leukaemia. The patient's brief explains that the sister is in remission having completed her treatment. If you had disclosed information about Ellen or had assumed that all the information from her was correct without listening to the patient in front of you, problems may have arisen. Did this happen to you? What would you do differently next time?

3 – Active listening and encouragement

Did you listen and give the patient time to talk?
Did you allow them to tell you why they were there?
If they were quiet, did you encourage them to talk using open questions?
Did you use any silence?

Did you listen, look and feel?

Did you listen to what they were saying?
Did you listen to what they were not saying?
Did you look and see how they behaved?
What was their body language saying?
Did you feel any emotions the patient gave out?
Did you feel any emotions evoked in you?
Were they depressed, angry, nervous or agitated?

If the patient stormed out of the room, why did they? What provoked that reaction? How would you ensure that this did not happen in the future?

If the patient became upset, how did you respond? What would you do next time?

4 – Relevant psychosocial information

One of the significant factors in this role play is that Mr/Mrs Gregory is not coping. Did you work that out? Did you ask?

Psychological
- *How are you coping?*
- *How is it affecting you?*
- *How are you sleeping at night?*

Financial
- *How are you coping having an extra person living with you?*
Mr/Mrs Gregory does not know about the daughter's debts. Did you divulge this information? If so, why?

Social
- *Do you have any support?*
- *Are you able to get any time for yourself?*

- *What do you do in your spare time?"*

<u>Spiritual</u>
- *Who do you confide in?*

5 – Expectations of the patient including any hidden agenda

Did you ask what the patient wanted?

- *How do you think I can help you today?*
- *What are you worried about?*
- *Is there anything else you would like to talk about?*

6 – Clinical questioning

There is clinical history to take in this case. You might want to ask a little more about the laxatives and change in behaviour of the daughter to help next time you see Ellen.

7 – Explanation and differential diagnosis

It is important to try to explain what anorexia is and ensure that Mr/Mrs Gregory knows that there are multiple agencies that can help; but at the present time, while Ellen has capacity, we cannot force any treatment onto her.

8 – Working diagnosis and management plan

If you managed to elicit the psychosocial information from the patient, you will hopefully have realised that Mr/Mrs Gregory is struggling to cope and needs help. If you didn't elicit this, ask yourself why. What else could you have asked to find out?

As a management plan there are several approaches:

a. *Support for Mr/Mrs Gregory*
   Your patient is distressed and needs ongoing support. You, the GP, are in a perfect position to provide continuity of care. Offer an appointment just for them in the next week and make sure that they know that there is support for them. It is very easy in this scenario to concentrate on the daughter and not offer mum/dad any support. Did

71

you fall into this trap? What could you do next time to ensure this doesn't happen?

b. *Support for the daughter*
The daughter clearly needs following up. She has missed appointments and now, with the added concerns of the parent, it appears that Ellen's problems could be more serious than they first appeared. Without breaching confidentiality, you need to support the parent and reassure them that you will offer the daughter an appointment. This can be done in many ways, including.

- Getting Mr/Mrs Gregory to talk to Ellen and ask her to come to the surgery either on her own or as a joint appointment with her parent.

- Offering to write to or call Ellen to request that she visits the surgery. You do not need to tell the parent that this will be a follow-up appointment.

9 – Patient choice

Did you ask the patient if they had any ideas about what they wanted?

- *What would you like us to do next?*
- *How do you think I can help you and Ellen?*

10 – Checking the patient's understanding

Did the patient understand? Did you ask? If not, why not?
Do they really know what anorexia is?

Remember it is not enough to assume they know what is happening. You need to *show* the assessors that you have asked.

11 – Follow-up and review as required

Whatever happens in your scenario, follow-up is important in this case both for Mr/Mrs Gregory and for Ellen. Make sure that you have articulated this and that the assessor knows your plans.

12 – Actor patient's general impression

You have hopefully covered this in your feedback, but do you think the patient will come back and see you? Do you think that Ellen will come and see you?

13 – Body language and physical interaction

- How was your eye contact?
- Are you a floor or ceiling thinker?
- Do you think you were too close/ too far away from the patient?
- Did you notice any irritating habits?
- If the patient became upset, did you touch them?
- Did this feel natural?
- What would you do next time?

14 – Remaining calm under pressure

- Were there any hairy moments?
- Did the patient get upset or angry?
- How did you respond to this?
- Did you feel that you were becoming emotionally involved, angry or irritated?
- What did you do to resolve it?
- What would you do next time?

There is a lot of information in the discussion and you may not have time to cover all of it in your role play. The discussion is there to point out all possible approaches and information that you could get from the scenario. Try rerunning it to see if you can practise other ways of approaching the patient to glean as much information as you can. The more you try and practise, the easier and the more natural it will feel on the day.

Doctor's Brief

You are a doctor in Accident and Emergency (A&E) and have just completed an arrest call on a 35-year-old patient called Hillary, who did not survive. Hillary's partner, who called the ambulance, had found the patient at home. When the paramedics arrived the patient had no pulse or spontaneous breathing. They attempted resuscitation but were unsuccessful. You were involved in the crash call in A&E and, after 45 minutes, your senior (who is now involved in another trauma call) stopped the resuscitation attempt. Hillary was declared dead 10 minutes ago.

Other information

The paramedics found two empty bottles of spirits and several empty medication bottles at his/her side. There was also an apparent suicide note.

Your senior colleague has asked you to inform the partner (Mr/Mrs Aristoula) who found Hillary unconscious at home and to try to get some background information to give to the coroner (we already have the patient's name and demographics).

(Please note: the name Hillary can be either female or male.)

ISCMEDICAL
Interview Skills Consulting

Use this box to make your pre-consultation notes

ROLE PLAY SCENARIO 4

Patient's Brief (Mr/Mrs Aristoula)

You are Mr/Mrs Aristoula, the long-term partner of Hillary (this name can be used both for a female or a male). You arrived home today and discovered Hillary lying in your bed, unconscious. You called the paramedics, who attempted to resuscitate. You last saw Hillary being wheeled into a room in A&E and are eagerly waiting to hear how he/she is.

Additional information

You know that Hillary has been depressed and under the care of the GP, in whom you have great trust. When you arrived home, you found two empty alcohol bottles on the bed. You did not see anything else and assume that Hillary was very drunk. He/she had been drinking increasing amounts over the last few weeks.

The doctor will tell you that Hillary is dead. If they use any other word or phrase, such as "passed away" or "not with us", play dumb and do not understand what they say. Only if they confirm that it is "death" or "died" should you respond. Be shocked and upset. After a few seconds, go very quiet and switch off from what the doctor is telling you. Only when they ask you a direct question should you re-enter the consultation. If the doctor does not try to re-engage you, do not volunteer anything. If they are compassionate and acknowledge that you are "zoned out", come back into the consultation.

If the doctor tries to tell you that it was suicide, show disbelief. There is no way that Hillary would do that. You did not see a suicide note. If asked, tell the doctor about the depression. Otherwise do not volunteer this information. Once the doctor confirms that empty drug bottles were found beside Hillary, start to blame yourself for the "suicide". You had a big fight this morning and stormed out. Allow the doctor to comfort you, but keep blaming yourself.

You have two small children and are frightened about how you are going to look after them. If the doctor offers suggestions of support, initially refuse. You will "be ok". If they suggest follow-up, agree only to go to your GP.

ROLE PLAY SCENARIO 4

Discussion

The first thing to do is read the brief. Read it and read it again. Did you do that? Did you get halfway through and forget something and have to refer back to the brief?

Next ask yourself: "What do I know from the brief?"

You know very little about the patient/ relative whom you are about to see and you have minimal information about Hillary. You know that Hillary is dead, and you know that you have to break this "bad news" to the relative. What was the cause of death? We don't know for sure, but all the information given points to suicide: the empty alcohol bottles, the empty medicine bottles and the suicide note.

Start to think about what you are going to say. How are you going to break the news? How long will you wait? What words will you use? What are the possible reactions? What will you do if the patient cries, shouts, collapses?

What other information do you require from the relative? Your senior has asked you for information to help the coroner. The brief states that we already have the patient demographics. You do not need to spend time finding out name, address and date of birth etc. Did you waste any time on these?

What sections and questions from the *Summary of proposed assessment criteria for role play* (p.36) could be relevant in this case? If you start to think of these before the patient comes in, you are more likely to ask the appropriate questions.

1 – Creating a safe environment

Did you move the furniture?
Were you sitting too close or too far away from the patient?
Was it comfortable?
Were there any tissues on the desk?

79

Were they close enough for you to reach to give to the patient?
Did you need to touch the patient to console them?
Were you close enough to do this comfortably?
How would you position the room differently next time?

2 – Introduction and putting the patient at ease

Did you use the patient's name? If not, why not? It was in the brief.

Did you get the patient to sit down or did the consultation start while you were both standing? How could you ensure that the patient was sitting comfortably before launching into the bad news? What would you do next time?

You have never met this patient before and you need to break the bad news as soon as is possible in the role play. Often, as doctors, we are scared of telling someone bad news and either ask a lot of introductory questions or let the patient run away with the consultation. You need to ensure that your demeanour is appropriate at the beginning of the consultation to give the patient an idea that it is bad news. There is nothing worse than the happy smiling doctor who greets the patient warmly and then launches into bad news. I'm not suggesting that you look like the grim reaper and change into your funeral clothes, but greeting the patient in a downbeat way creates an atmosphere that will start to prepare them for the worst.

The sooner you can confirm a patient's worst fears the better but this needs to be judged carefully. If the patient asks, "Is Hillary all right?" then you need to be honest and, in that case, saying "No" may be enough to start with. Some people would launch into the whole information at this point and this may be appropriate in some cases.

Often, allowing the patient to lead the rate of information given to them works very well. This type of approach is likely to lead onto further questions such as: "Why what's wrong?", "How bad is it?", "Tell me the worst", "Is he/she dead?" If the patient does not ask these types of question it is important to move on and break the news as soon as you can.

Every case of "breaking bad news" is different and there is no strict formula to follow. In general, you need to gauge how much the patient

knows and then gently break the news to them in a clear and coherent way.

What words did you use? You will notice from the brief that Mr/Mrs Aristoula has been instructed not to understand unless you said the words "dead" or "died". This is good practice to get into. It is of course acceptable to use softer words such as "passed away", "passed on" and "no longer with us" but it is always important to clarify that the patient understands that this means dead or died. There have been cases where a relative has been told that their loved one was "no longer with us", only for them to ask: "Why, where have you transferred them to?"

Avoid putting yourself in this position by being clear and direct, but by giving the information to the patient in a way that they can cope with and understand.

Remember, do not assume anything. Do not add any information to the brief unless the patient tells you that information. Just like in real life, the only things we know about our patients are written down or told to us during a consultation. We don't make things up in the hospital/ clinic. Don't do it in the role play.

It is also important not to assume that the patient in front of you knows everything that you do. Did you assume that the relative knew about the suicide note or the pills? The patient thought that their relative was drunk and had no idea that it was suicide. How did you manage this?

3 – Active listening and encouragement

After breaking the bad news, this is the main aspect of the consultation.

Did you listen and give the patient time to talk?
Did you allow them room to take in the information?
If they were quiet, did you encourage them to talk using open questions?

The patient was instructed in the brief to "switch off" and only come back into the consultation if actively encouraged to do so. Did you notice that they had switched off? What did you do to bring them back in?

If a patient disengages from a consultation it is usually obvious. In the role-play situation the actor patient will give you big clues that they have

switched off. They may look away from you, look to the floor or ceiling. They may hold their head in their hands. Remember to listen, look and feel.

Look and watch your actor patient. Remember that they are trying to help you. If you watch their body language you will know how they are responding. Try it in your own clinical practice over the next few days. Watch the patient. It is amazing how much you learn from their non-verbal communication.

There are always candidates who do not notice that the patient has switched off. Was that you? How long did you carry on talking before noticing? If you did notice, did you use any silence?

Did you listen, look and feel?

Did you listen to what they were saying?
Did you listen to what they were not saying?
Did you look and see how they behaved?
What was their body language saying?
Did you feel any emotions the patient gave out?
Did you feel any emotions evoked in you?
Were they upset, angry, nervous or agitated?

If the patient became upset, how did you respond?
What would you do next time?
If your patient was angry, why do you think they were angry?
What did you do or say to ease their fears?

Often, reflecting back a patient's emotion helps to alleviate a difficult situation.

- *I can see you are really upset.*
- *It is ok to be upset.*
- *I can see that you are angry, can you tell me why?*

The other approach is to use silence. Sometimes saying nothing will give the patient the room and space to vent their feelings. Active listening is often all that is required.

An alternative is to ask the patient how you can help alleviate their emotions.

- *I can see you are really angry, what can I do to help?*
- *It is ok to be upset. Can I do anything for you?*

The good old British "cup of tea" is often used in difficult situations and you can always suggest this in your role play. Remember, do everything that you would normally do in practice. The actor patient is likely to say no but at least you have offered.

- *Can I get you anything? A glass of water, tea?*

4 – Relevant psychosocial information

Your senior colleague had asked you to get some information for the coroner, but the psychosocial impact on Mr/Mrs Aristoula is also important.

Psychological
- What state of mind was Hillary in?
- Did you find out that Hillary had been suffering from depression and had consulted the GP?
- Were there any signs of self-harm or attempted suicide? This may have raised difficulties as Mr/Mrs Aristoula did not know about the suicide note. How did you break this to them? Did you assume that they already knew? Do you think that your approach made things easier or more difficult? What would you do next time?
- How is Mr/Mrs Aristoula coping with the news? You can find this out by watching (listen, look and feel), but also by asking "How are you?" or "Are you all right?"

Financial
This is probably not relevant in this consultation, although you could ask if Mr/Mrs Aristoula works.

Social
- *Do you have any support?*
- *Can I call anyone for you?*
- *Who is at home with you?*

If you do not ask this specific question you may not find out that there are two young children at home. Did you get this information? What about support for the children?

<u>Spiritual</u>
- *Who do you confide in?*

It may also be useful to ask if they would like you to call the hospital chaplain. All hospitals have a chapel and on-call religious staff covering all faiths.

5 – Expectations of the patient including any hidden agenda

This section is not relevant to this role play.

6 – Clinical questioning

You may want to know a little about Hillary's behaviour in the preceding days. A simple suicide risk could be undertaken. This would include:

- Previous suicide attempts
- Any warnings given to friends or family
- Mood in the preceding days
- Family problems
- Financial problems
- Work situation
- Was there anyone expected to return or was the suicide performed when Hillary knew they wouldn't be found until it was too late.

7 – Explanation and differential diagnosis

It is important to try to explain what happened clearly so that Mr/Mrs Aristoula understands fully. You may also want to inform them that the coroner will be informed about this death. It is likely that Hillary's death was suicide, but this will be confirmed later on. If you are asked a difficult question that you do not know the answer to, it is important that you are honest and say that you don't know. You can always offer to find out and come back to them.

ISCMEDICAL

Interview Skills Consulting

8 – Working diagnosis and management plan

We know the likely cause is suicide and hopefully you worked out that Mr/Mrs Aristoula blames themself and that they are worried about coping with their two young children.

In terms of a management plan, there are several approaches:

a. *Support for Mr/Mrs Aristoula*
   Your patient is distressed and needs both immediate and ongoing support. In the short term, you could offer a nurse to come and sit with them. Offer to call a friend or relative and tell them that you will telephone their GP to let them know.

   You should have picked up on the fact that Hillary had a good relationship with the GP. You could offer to telephone the GP ensuring that they are kept in the loop. Many GPs will contact bereaved patients and ask them to come into the surgery for a review. This is even more important with suicide here as there are often many unanswered questions.

b. *Support for the children*
   Having two young children and being recently bereaved is very distressing; and, although often the children give the bereaved parent something to focus on, it is important that the children are not put at risk. Try to ensure that there will be someone at home with the family overnight or suggest that they go and stay with a friend or family. By informing the GP, you can ensure that there is a professional who will be aware of potential problems.

   If the children are under 5, it is also worth informing the health visitor. If the children are in school, you can telephone the school to inform them.

   By ensuring that there is support for the family it may ease the difficulties face by them, ultimately helping their grieving process.

9 – Patient choice

Patient choice is important particularly relating to who to talk to and who to inform.

85

10 – Checking the patient's understanding

Did the patient understand? Did you ask? If not, why not? Remember it is not enough to assume they know what is happening. You need to *show* the assessors that you have asked.

11 – Follow-up and review as required

Whatever happened in your scenario, follow-up is important. Make sure that you have articulated this and that the assessor knows your plans for follow up with the GP.

12 – Actor patient's general impression

You have hopefully covered this in your feedback, but do you think the patient will remember you as a good doctor?
Did you ease their grief in any way?

13 – Body language and physical interaction

- How was your eye contact?
- Are you a floor or ceiling thinker?
- Do you think you were too close/ too far away from the patient?
- Did you notice any irritating habits?
- If the patient became upset, did you touch them?
- Did this feel natural?
- What would you do next time?

14 – Remaining calm under pressure

- Were there any hairy moments?
- Did the patient get upset or angry?
- How did you respond to this?
- Did you feel yourself becoming emotionally involved, angry or irritated? What did you do to resolve it?
- What would you do next time?

There is a lot of information in the discussion and you may not have time to cover all of it in your role play. The discussion is there to point out all possible approaches and information that you could get from the scenario. Try rerunning it to see if you can practise other ways of approaching the patient to

glean as much information as you can. The more you try and practise, the easier and the more natural it will feel on the day.

ROLE PLAY SCENARIO 5

Doctor's Brief

You are working in paediatrics and recently saw a 10-year-old boy called Gianni with his main carer (Mr/Mrs Evans). He was referred for a psychosocial problem, which resulted in him avoiding school. After numerous consultations with Gianni and the main carer, you have discharged Gianni from your clinic with a behavioural programme that appears to be working. Both the paediatric team and the main carer are happy with Gianni's treatment and progress.

You recently received a distressed call from the main carer stating that their estranged husband/wife is going to come up to the hospital demanding to see the Consultant as they believe that Gianni needs some kind of investigation in the form of a CT scan to rule out a brain tumour causing the change in Gianni's behaviour. The main carer is happy for you to share all the information.

Your Consultant does not think that any investigation is required and will be unavailable for the rest of the day.

The estranged spouse has now come to you. You are the only doctor available to talk to him/her.

ISCMEDICAL
Interview Skills Consulting

Use this box to make your pre-consultation notes

ROLE PLAY SCENARIO 5

Patient's Brief (Mr/Mrs Evans, the estranged spouse)

You are Mr/Mrs Evans and have a 10-year-old son called Gianni. You split up from your husband/wife 3 years ago and Gianni lives with them. You do not live with Gianni. He only comes to stay with you at weekends and you have noticed that he is withdrawn and you know that he has not been attending school.

Your best friend was diagnosed with a brain tumour 6 months ago and has just died. Do not tell the doctor this unless you are asked about your worries, but your main concern is that Gianni has a brain tumour too. Before your friend was diagnosed, they became withdrawn, agoraphobic and had significant personality changes. Your friend was diagnosed late and was unfit for surgery. You do not want Gianni to die and want everything done that is possible. You are willing to pay privately to have a scan.

There are big issues between you and your estranged partner and deep down you know that this is affecting Gianni's behaviour. If the doctor suggests that this may be the cause of the problem, become verbally aggressive and accuse them of not treating your son properly.

You are adamant that your son needs a CT scan of his head and are not happy that you have not been involved in the hospital management.

From the start, be angry and demand to see the Consultant unless the doctor explains clearly that they can help. Demand also that your son has a CT scan of his head. Only calm down if the doctor is compassionate and recognises your distress. If they communicate well, you will accept that the CT scan is not required and realise that there are risks with radiation if the medical profession does tests that are not indicated.

Accept any offer of help relating to talking about your friend's death and relationship counselling to help Gianni with his behaviour.

ROLE PLAY SCENARIO 5

Discussion

The first thing to do is read the brief. Read it and read it again. Did you do that? Did you get halfway through and forget something and have to refer back to the brief?

Next ask yourself: "What do I know from the brief?"

You know that you are the only doctor available to talk to the parent of Gianni. You know that your Consultant has been involved with the care of the child and has diagnosed a behavioural problem causing school avoidance. You know that this is improving with a behaviour programme. You know that one parent (the main carer, who is not present today) is happy with the care that has been provided.

From the brief, the main carer has warned you that the estranged "weekend" parent is coming to see you and wants a CT scan for Gianni. You know that their worry is one of a brain tumour.

You also know that they want to see the Consultant.

Start to think about why this parent is coming to see you. What has made them come now, after the child has been discharged?

What potential difficulties might arise during this scenario?

What sections and questions from the *Summary of proposed assessment criteria for role play* (p.36) could be relevant in this case? If you start to think of these before the patient comes in, you are more likely to ask the appropriate questions.

1 – Creating a safe environment

Did you move the furniture?
Were you sitting too close or too far away from the patient?
Was it comfortable?

2 – Introduction and putting the patient at ease

Did you use the patient's name? If not, why not? It was in the brief.

You have never met this patient before and so starting the consultation with a general open question would be most appropriate.

- *Hello Mr/Mrs Evans. How can I help?*
- *We've not met before, I'm Dr _____. What can I do for you today?*

By asking such open questions you allow the patient to talk, ensuring that you find out exactly why they have come to see you. In this case it is for a specific demand. Mr/Mrs Evans is angry and wants a CT scan for their child.

One way of dealing with an angry patient who is making demands is by acknowledging their anger and continuing to ask open questions.

- *You are obviously very worried about Gianni.*
- *What are your biggest fears / worries?*

If the patient keeps asking for the CT scan, then acknowledging this without agreeing to it will allow you to move the conversation forward.

- *You've said you think Gianni needs a CT scan. Before we talk about that, can I ask you some other questions?*
- *You would obviously like Gianni to have a CT scan. Can I ask why you would like that?*

Remember, do not assume anything. Do not add any information to the brief unless the patient tells you that information. Just like in real life, the only things we know about our patients are written down or told to us during a consultation. We don't make things up in the hospital/ clinic. Don't do it in the role play.

It is important in this scenario to work out exactly what this parent knows. This is easy to find out by asking the right questions.

- *Do you know why Gianni was referred to us?*
- *Can you tell me what you know already about Gianni's care?*

The other issue that may be raised at the beginning of the consultation is the patient's request to talk to the Consultant. This can be difficult to deal with if you are a junior doctor; but being honest and offering an apology is always the best start.

- *I'm sorry, Mr/Mrs Evans. The Consultant is not in the hospital today. I am Dr _____. I work very closely with the Consultant and have been involved in your son's care.*
- *I'm sorry. Unfortunately, the Consultant is unavailable. I could offer to book you an appointment with him later in the week if you would like, but perhaps I can help in some way?*

Offering an appointment with the Consultant shows that you are being open and that the Consultant is willing to talk to Mr/Mrs Evans. If you were clear and compassionate, your actor patient should have calmed down a little by now. Did they?

If they remained angry, why do you think this was?
What could you have done differently to alleviate their concerns and help calm them down?
What would you do differently next time?

3 – Active listening and encouragement

Did you listen and give the patient time to talk?
Did you allow them to tell you why they were there?

If they were quiet, did you encourage them to talk using open questions?
Did you use any silence?
How did you respond to the anger?

Often, when our patients are angry, we meet that anger by talking too much and trying to talk over the patient. If you remain silent and actively listen, the patient will rapidly run out of steam, which will make the consultation easier. Have you ever tried to have a heated discussion or

argument with someone who refuses to be drawn into it? How quickly did you give up?

Did you listen, look and feel?

Did you listen to what they were saying?
Did you listen to what they were not saying?
Did you look and see how they behaved?
What was their body language saying?
Did you feel any emotions the patient gave out?
Did you feel any emotions evoked in you?
Did the anger make you feel angry, intimidated or anxious?
How did you respond?
What would you do next time?

4 – Relevant psychosocial information

There is a significant psychosocial component to this role play. Mr/Mrs Evans is scared that their son has a brain tumour. They have just seen their best friend die from this condition and assume that all personality changes are due to the same cause. Did you find this out? If not, why not?

Psychological
- *How is Gianni's behaviour affecting you?*
- *How are you coping with it?*

Financial
This is not really important in this case although the patient may offer to go privately. This may allow you to ask how they would be able to afford private health care.

Social
- *Do you have any support?*
- *Are you able to share your worries with anyone?*

Spiritual
- *Who do you confide in?*

ISCMEDICAL
Interview Skills Consulting

5 – Expectations of the patient including any hidden agenda

You probably did not need to ask what the patient wanted as they demanded the CT scan. Did you explore why they wanted it?

- *What do you expect the CT scan to show?*
- *How do you think that the CT scan will help Gianni?*

6 – Clinical questioning

You may want to briefly cover the behavioural symptoms that Gianni expresses and ask about fits, faints and funny turns, although this will have been covered in consultation with Gianni.

7 – Explanation and differential diagnosis

It is important to try to explain that the current working diagnosis for Gianni is related to a pure behavioural problem and that he has been fully assessed by the team including the Consultant and that, with his current management, he appears to be improving. You could enquire about possible causes for his behaviour problem but be careful not to apportion blame.

You need to reassure that if there were any concerns about his symptoms pointing to something more sinister then he would have been investigated. He is not deteriorating and appears to be getting better. There are no symptoms suggesting an underlying pathology.

8 – Working diagnosis and management plan

The main management is to ensure that Mr/Mrs Evans is happy with your explanation. If you discovered that their friend died recently from a brain tumour you could explore issues relating to their grieving process.

They are clearly upset about their friend's death, which is influencing their reactions to their son's problems. Offering a support service for Mr/Mrs Evans to explore these feeling of grief may help. This can include their own GP or support networks such as Cruse Bereavement Care.

It is important to acknowledge the family difficulties and suggest ways of talking to both parents together. You could offer a joint appointment with

you, or with the Consultant on their return, with both parents to explore the concerns further. It may be that their relationship is good enough for them to sit down and talk together either alone or with Gianni's GP.

9 – Patient choice

This has been covered in point 5, but you could ask the patient what they want to happen next.

10 – Checking the patient's understanding

Did the patient understand?
Did you ask? If not, why not?

Remember it is not enough to assume they know what is happening. You need to *show* the assessors that you have asked.

11 – Follow-up and review as required

Whatever happened in your scenario, follow-up is important both to ensure that all the patient's concerns regarding their son have been resolved, but also regarding their grief for their friend. Subsequent appointments with the GP, you or the Consultant could also address the family dynamics and possible cause for behavioural change in Gianni.

Offering bereavement support using the appropriate resources is also important in this case.

12 – Actor patient's general impression

You have hopefully covered this in your feedback, but do you think the patient was satisfied with your explanation?
Do you think that they will need to come back and see the Consultant or were they happy with your reassurance?

13 – Body language and physical interaction

How was your eye contact?
Are you a floor or ceiling thinker?
Do you think you were too close/ too far away from the patient?
Did you notice any irritating habits?
If the patient became upset, did you touch them? Did this feel natural? What would you do next time?
If the patient was aggressive, did you find yourself moving away? How did you cope? Did your nerves or anxiety show to the observer or to the patient?

14 – Remaining calm under pressure

Were there any hairy moments?
Did the patient get upset or angry?
How did you respond to this?
Did you feel yourself becoming emotionally involved, angry or irritated?
What did you do to resolve it?
What would you do next time?

There is a lot of information in the discussion and you may not have time to cover all of it in your role play. The discussion is there to point out all possible approaches and information that you could get from the scenario. Try rerunning it to see if you can practise other ways of approaching the patient to glean as much information as you can. The more you try and practise, the easier and the more natural it will feel on the day.

Group discussions

The second of the tasks that you will be assessed on at your selection centre is the group discussion. You will usually be working with three or four other candidates as your colleagues within a meeting environment. I mentioned earlier that the other candidates are competitors for the job but you still need to respect them and behave courteously. By the time you reach Stage 3 of the selection process, the ratio of candidates to jobs is often 2:1 or better, so many of those candidates will become your colleagues in the future. It is therefore well worth starting to build relationships as soon as you arrive at the selection centre.

The other candidates

Your interaction with your colleagues is formally assessed within the group discussion. Anything that you can do to make this "meeting" run smoothly will be advantageous. One example of how to influence the dynamics within the group would be to know them a little before the task begins. Try to work out which candidates you will be working with during your assessment and start to build a relationship with them. Learn their names before the task begins; have an informal chat. This is not always going to be possible but if it is then do it.

If the selection centre gives you a timetable with the candidate numbers of all those who should be in the same room with you during the group discussion and all the candidates are wearing a badge with their numbers on them, use your coffee break or initial waiting time to seek out your group. You only need a few minutes with each person to learn his or her name and introduce yourself. Don't waste any opportunity that is available to you. It would clearly be inappropriate for the group to get together and plan the session in advance and I also believe that this would be impossible to do. However, if you already know the names of the candidates within your group and have smiled at each other, I am certain that you will work much better as an overall group.

I will discuss in more detail the assessment criteria, but be aware that you are being tested on your teamwork. It is therefore important for the whole team to be on a level footing at the beginning of the exercise. If you are able to work out who is who, introduce the rest of the group to one another so that the whole team is starting from the same level of knowledge. Don't risk trying to appear smart by slyly gaining knowledge about the rest of your group. It is likely to count against you if it appears that you have sneaked around gaining

unfair knowledge which places the other candidates in the group at a disadvantage. Think TEAM.

Well-run courses specifically aimed at the GPST Stage 3 selection centre will give you the opportunity to practise. You cannot get this experience from a book. The more you practise, the easier the exercise will become and the more confidence you will have on the day. If you cannot attend a course, at least try the exercises given in this book with a group of friends or colleagues. Ideally, you will need at least one person to observe and give you objective feedback but bear in mind that those who know you well may not always be as objective as they need to be to help you improve.

What will happen?

Read the information sent to you from your selection centre/ deanery for definitive clarification. Most centres will allow 20 minutes to complete the group discussion exercise. Some centres may only have 10 minutes if they are based on the OSCE set-up. The principles are the same.

The number of candidates within each "meeting" may vary from centre to centre, but there are usually four. For the purposes of this chapter I will work on the assumption that there are four candidates.

At the scheduled time, you will be escorted into the meeting room with the other candidates in your group. The room will already be set-up. Inside will be four chairs – usually around a table. Often, there are paper and pens on the table but this is something to check when you arrive. There will also be a number of assessors. Usually one per candidate, but some centres may have one assessor for two candidates. These are GP examiners or educational psychologists who are trained to mark you by the strict criteria of the selection centre. Be polite when you enter but ignore them. They are there to mark you, not to help, guide or advise you. If they cannot see you, they will move. Try to forget that they are present. You may hear them writing throughout the whole assessment. Try to ignore it.

Figure 5. Typical room set-up (assuming 4 candidates and 4 assessors)

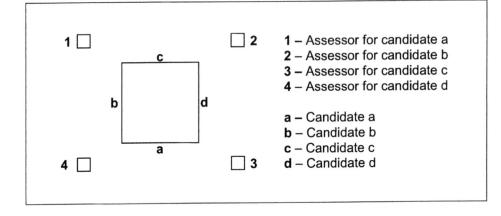

1 – Assessor for candidate a
2 – Assessor for candidate b
3 – Assessor for candidate c
4 – Assessor for candidate d

a – Candidate a
b – Candidate b
c – Candidate c
d – Candidate d

Figure 6. Typical room set-up (assuming 4 candidates and 2 assessors)

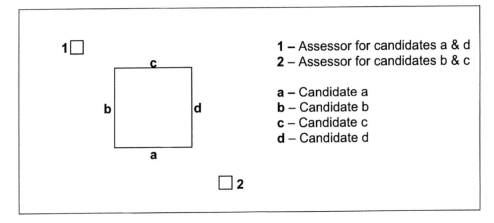

1 – Assessor for candidates a & d
2 – Assessor for candidates b & c

a – Candidate a
b – Candidate b
c – Candidate c
d – Candidate d

Read the brief

On the day of the assessment, you will be given 5 minutes to read the brief. This time may be outside the room prior to the start of the assessment, but often it is inside the examination room once everyone is seated. Read it and read it again. This is just like an agenda for any other meeting that you will have attended.

The issues around which the discussions will revolve will be related to primary or secondary care in the NHS. If you are an overseas candidate or have not worked in the NHS, you will need to read around the key areas suggested later. Keep an eye on the medical and the national press.

Anything is possible in this exercise, but remember that you are not being assessed on your expertise in a certain subject. You are being assessed on your TEAMwork and group interactions.

1 – Simple group discussion

The brief is usually something very vague, for example:

> *You are four senior house officers (SHOs) / Foundation Year 2 (FY2) doctors on the "Mess party committee". Discuss how you would organise the next hospital ball.*

All doctors are at the same level and as a group you are all given the same information and told to discuss the issues raised. This is the simplest type of discussion with issues relating to primary or secondary care. Other possible topics include: audits, ethical dilemmas, setting up a meeting, service or teaching session, and handling a complaint.

2 – Extended simple group discussion

The extended simple group discussion is becoming increasingly common. The brief has a simple opening, followed by a lengthy explanation of a case to be covered. It can extend over two A4 pages, for example:

> *You are four SHOs/ FY2 doctors at the hospital's "significant events" meeting. You are asked to discuss the death of a patient, following a relative's complaint and threat of legal action.*

The brief would then give you a copy of the relative's letter of complaint, the deceased patient's history, the ward nurses' and doctors' perspectives on the case and the hospital lawyer's response.

3 – Extended complicated group discussion

This type of group discussion is also increasingly being used. The brief typically consists of a common opening statement but then each candidate will be given a different piece of information that they need to discuss within the group. For example:

> *You are four doctors at meeting. You are all at the same grade. There is a problem with the hospital budget and you have four patients, who need expensive treatment, but do not have the budget for all of them.*

Each candidate will be given the case history of one of those patients. As a team you need to discuss all four patients' cases and make a decision as to which two patients should get their treatment.

- *Candidate A is given a detailed brief on a 34-year-old patient with two children and Rheumatoid arthritis requiring a new drug costing £8000 per year.*

- *Candidate B is given a detailed brief on a 2-year-old girl who requires a bone marrow transplant costing £24,000.*

- *Candidate C is given a detailed brief on a 68-year-old heavy smoker who needs long-term oxygen therapy costing £12,000.*

- *Candidate D is given a detailed brief on a couple that need infertility treatment costing £7,000.*

  Note: all costs are fictitious.

4 – Role-specific discussion

This type of group discussion is not common, generally speaking, but some deaneries have used it recently.

The brief consists of a common opening statement, with each member of the group being allocated a different role to play.

For example:

> *You are a group of four SHOs/ FY2 doctors who have decided to set up a smoking cessation service.*
>
> *Candidate A will play the role of a doctor.*
> *Candidate B will be a nurse practitioner.*
> *Candidate C will be a health service manager.*
> *Candidate D will be a patient representative.*

You are then asked to discuss setting up the service from the point of view of the person you represent.

Asking you to play the role of someone who is in a different job makes the scenario complicated. You need to ensure that you know a little about the health professions in a multidisciplinary team.

5 – The presentation

This is simply an extension of the group discussion. Do not panic if you are told that you have a presentation group discussion. You do not need to prepare anything or be an IT whizz. Your group discussion will proceed as normal, but added to the brief will be a question that the group needs to answer through a presentation.

For example: the group discussion is based on a new drug including the cost implications and side effects. The final part of the brief might say:

> *You need to decide whether you will prescribe this drug and present your decision to a patient representative.*

This is testing your ability to assimilate information from the discussion and present it in a coherent way. Each candidate will go to an assessor at

the end of the group discussion and individually present the group's findings to them. The important things to remember are that:

a.   *You are representing the group not your own opinion*
Remember that the assessor has heard the whole discussion and knows what decision was made.

b.   *Communication skills will be assessed*
Who are you presenting to? Make sure that you use appropriate language. You will not be using the same language when presenting to an expert that you would use when presenting to a patient. Pitch the presentation correctly.

c.   *You should be prepared to answer questions*
The assessor may ask you questions on the presentation of your opinion. Be honest. Base them on the group opinion and, if you do not know, tell the truth: "I'm sorry I do not have that information. I could get back to you after our next meeting and clarify things."

Preparation time

During your 5 minutes' preparation, make some notes if there is time. Write down any ideas that arise as you read. You can refer back to these notes throughout the "meeting" to ensure that you cover everything that you can. Make sure that the brief is visible at all times to remind you of the purpose of the exercise. It is amazing how easy it is to run away with yourself during this task, only to realise that at the end of the 20 minutes you have not answered the question posed to you.

Answer the question

Ensure that you cover what is stated in the brief. If there is a question posed, answer it. Cover every aspect that is mentioned in the brief. In an ideal situation, by the end of the allotted time you will have reached a conclusion as a group. If you haven't, don't panic. The majority of the points to be scored in this exercise will be for your teamwork and participation rather than the factual content and conclusion. It is unlikely that there will be a right or wrong answer, so make sure that you justify any conclusions that are made.

How to behave

The most important thing here is to be yourself but to "play the game". You need to score points as a TEAM. You can only do this by working together as constructively as is possible. Everyone in your team is an important member of the group and should be respected, even if you do not agree with what they are saying. Whatever you do, do not play a character. Don't try to be something that you are not. If you are a natural leader, attempt to lead the discussion; if you are not a natural leader, don't try to become one overnight. Be yourself but "play the game".

Be heard

It is important to be heard not only by the members of the group, but also by the assessors. If they cannot hear you, it will be difficult to award you the points that you deserve. Be clear and audible.

The different roles within a group

There are many roles that one can adopt in a team and I have summarised the main types below. As you read through the following descriptions, think about which "role" you automatically take in life and at work.

You will be expected to be yourself and, to be successful, you will also be required to understand and adapt to the other personalities that make up the jigsaw of "the group". We do not always fit into one stereotype and so you may find that you fit into several categories. This is a very good trait to have as it makes you flexible and adaptable to changing situations.

1 – The leader

The leader tries (not always successfully) to run the meeting. It would be similar to the chairperson at a formal meeting. In group exercises, the "leadership" is often handed from person to person rather than a defined person organising the whole talk.

Examples of how the leader would participate:
- *So let's get started. We have 20 minutes to cover…*
- *Who would like to go first? Does anyone else have any ideas?*
- *I would like to thank everyone for their input and call this meeting to a close.*

2 – The facilitator

The facilitator tends to guide the discussion and organise the structure of the talk. They may not contribute a large amount to the discussion in the form of ideas, but help guide and organise the information being discussed. They also tend to mediate when conflicts develop.

Examples of how the facilitator would participate:

- *Now that we've started talking, can I summarise the points that we need to cover?*
- *We appear to have finished talking about the organisation. Can I suggest that we go onto talking about how we will fund this?*
- *We only appear to have 5 minutes left, do you think we should summarise what we have done so far?*

Comment

The roles of leader and facilitator are often combined but not always so. If you are a natural leader or facilitator by all means use your talents within the group exercise and show your strengths, but remember that there may be other leaders within the group. You may believe that you are the best person for the role, but unless your team agrees and responds to you as leader you will clearly not be working as a TEAM member. Most of the points for this exercise are relating to your ability to work with and respond to others.

3 – The ideas person

The ideas people are the ones who do not try to run the meeting, but come up with useful ideas and plans to make the meeting a success.

Ideas people can be of two types: those who are loud and push forward many ideas, or they can be the quieter member of the group who does not speak often but, when they do, the whole group listens and the discussion is moved significantly forward. Think about the last time you were at a clinical meeting. Can you think of the person who remained reasonably quiet but every time they spoke something profound was raised?

4 – Supporters

The supporters are those people who do not fit into any of the above groups and may not have a huge number of ideas but, once a point has

been raised, continue the discussion forward, developing a concrete plan. They also tend to agree and support the rest of the team by acknowledging any input and encouraging further discussion.

The ideal situation

All teams need both leaders and members to be efficient. The same applies in your group discussion. If there are three leaders and only one ideas person, the discussion will not be as effective as in a group that has one leader, two ideas people and a facilitator. The reverse is also true. If you have four ideas people and no leader, the discussion is likely to be unstructured, disjointed and subsequently less effective.

For me, the most important quality to possess in any team/ group exercise is the ability to change one's role and to adapt to the rest of the team. By having the flexibility to fit into any of the roles suggested above in response to the situation and types of people that you encounter, you are likely to be a better team player. In the context of the group discussion assessment, this is what I mean by "playing the game".

Example 1

Let's assume that you are a natural leader and regularly run meetings of your own at work. One of the participants in your group exercise is domineering and is determined to lead the group despite no one else agreeing to it. You have two choices: you can either stand firm and fight for the leadership knowing that you will do a far better job, or you can rapidly adapt your own role and become a facilitator, supporter or ideas person. Think TEAM. What would be better for the whole group performance: a fight between two members of the group or one "leader" bowing down gracefully, allowing an adequate discussion and completion of the task?

Example 2

Let's assume that you are usually a supporter in meetings and at work. In your group, you rapidly realise that there are three supporters and one ideas person. If you know about the other roles and are adaptable and flexible, then, by taking on a facilitator and/or a leader role, you can save your group discussion and make it more successful. Think TEAM. What would be better for the whole group performance? A potentially unstructured and rambling

discussion or you stepping out of your comfort zone to facilitate the group as a whole?

Playing the game

In the two examples above, I am not suggesting that you change your personality or "play-act a character". What I am suggesting is being flexible, adaptable and responsive to the personalities of the people around you.

In summary, do not go into the group discussion with a fixed idea of what your role in the group *will* be. Decide what you would *like* it to be, but be ready to adapt for the benefit of the whole team.

Time management

You are usually expected to mark your own time. In most centres you will have 20 minutes to complete the task and, at the end, you will be asked to leave the room. If your centre runs the OSCE-type assessment, there will be a bell at the end signalling you to move onto the next station. Take with you a watch or desk clock that you can easily see without distracting you from the conversation. Consider offering to monitor the time. Make sure that someone in the group points out when you have 5 minutes left. This is the time to summarise and round up the discussion, attempt to come to a conclusion and ensure that you have answered the whole question posed to the group. If you do offer to monitor the time yourself, please make sure that you are not "clock watching" and removing yourself from the TEAM and from the discussion.

Time management and working under time pressure will be assessed. You need to be particularly attentive if all candidates have different information in the brief. Use your time well and make sure that everyone has time and space to present their own information and their own ideas. In addition, ensure that you allow some time at the end to summarise and conclude your findings. Above all, make sure that you have time to answer the question.

Time management cannot be your own individual responsibility. It has to be the responsibility of the whole team. Don't spend the whole assessment marking time and moving people on. If you do this, your will score the points for one aspect of the assessment, but miss all the other available points. Balance the responsibility amongst the group. It may be an idea to remind your group at the start of the assessment that time is limited and that you must all make sure that the discussion moves on to a conclusion before the

end. This can be done before you even enter the room, during the 5 minutes of preparation or even at the beginning of the discussion.

How to start the discussion

The beginning of any group discussion in an examination environment is always difficult. You may have found time to introduce yourself to the other candidates and know their names as suggested earlier but you do not know about the personalities, strengths and weaknesses of the other candidates.

There is often a very awkward silence at the beginning where everyone is wondering who will start first. You may decide that you will burst in with an opening remark to avoid the silence, but other people in the group may have the same idea and you may find that you all start together! If there is a silence – even if you are not a natural leader – it is worth thinking of a way to open the discussion.

- *I'm not sure of everyone's name. Can we go round and introduce ourselves?*
- *We all know each other, shall we get started?*
- *We have 20 minutes to cover rather a lot, shall I start?*
- *Does anyone have any experience of this subject?*

There are many other ways of beginning the discussion and, often, once it has started it flows beautifully. Have something to say "just in case". Develop something that is natural for you and flows easily. Practise at work, at home or when you are standing waiting for a bus, train or tube. The more you practise, the easier it will be on the day.

Common difficulties encountered

1 – The quiet colleague

You
Remember that this is a group exercise and that you will be marked on your participation within the group. If you are normally quiet and reserved, make an effort to participate. You do not need to be the leader; you can simply be a supporter by acknowledging and encouraging. If you don't say anything, you are unlikely to score well.

Another candidate
If you have a quiet member in your group and you allow them to sit and not participate then you are not working as an efficient TEAM member. It is everyone's responsibility in the group to ensure that all candidates have a platform to speak and to be heard. Try to encourage others and ask for opinions.

- *Joanne, what do you think of that?*
- *Darren, do you have a preference?*

Be careful not to trap a quiet and reserved candidate into a corner. Suggesting to someone that they should summarise the discussion or come up with the next topic may send them into a panic if they have no ideas or have not been listening to the conversation. It will of course reflect badly on them, but also more importantly it may present you in a bad light, as someone who embarrassed a colleague (even if it was unintentional).

There are candidates who will just not join in, even when encouraged. If this happens to you, be seen to keep trying but don't spend all you energy on them either.

The worst thing that can happen is that three candidates get closer and closer with the fourth, quiet, colleague left staring at the ceiling. This would not be a successful outcome.

2 – The loud colleague

Some people do not know when to stop talking. These candidates can be in a leader, facilitator or an ideas role and just love the sound of their own voice. It can be very difficult to manage but, again, think of the TEAM. Is it better to stand up and fight or would you appear a better team member if you keep chipping away very slowly, helping them to understand what is happening, whilst supporting the rest of the group?

You
If you are the type of person who tends to talk a lot, or who always takes the lead, just take a step back and think about the TEAM. You may believe that you are the best candidate and have all the good ideas, but this task is about you interacting with the whole group. Are you listening to others? Is there someone else who looks like they would like to take over

for a while? Try offering the lead to other people. They may not take it, but at least you will be seen to be trying.

The worst group discussion that I witnessed involved one senior experienced doctor who had decided that he was the best person to lead the discussion, not realising that a very junior member of the team wanted to take the lead. The other two members of the team tried to facilitate the discussion, but the experienced doctor was so dominant that he ended up taking over and talking for 10 minutes before noticing that the more junior doctor had disengaged from the group.

Look at the other candidates and their body language during the discussion. If everyone is included and happy, it will be evident from their behaviour and their body language. If people are looking away, disengaging or, worse, talking between themselves, then something is going wrong. Be aware of your group and think TEAM.

Another candidate
If you face a situation where one member of the group is taking over and others in the group are uncomfortable, there are ways to ease the awkwardness that it creates.

Try opening the floor to others:

- *Asim, I'm not sure that I agree with you on every point. What do you think, Sarah?*

By doing this, you are bringing another voice into the conversation. This often reminds the dominant colleague that there are other people around.

Try changing the subject:

- *I've noticed that we are halfway through our time. Does anyone mind if I summarise where we are up to?*

If everything else has failed you may need to be more direct:

- *Paula, you have some very good arguments, but would you mind if we went round the table and got everyone else's point of view?*

By all means, try your best to avoid a conflict, but it is important that everyone in the TEAM is happy and able to participate.

3 – Conflict

It is highly unlikely that you will agree with everything that is said in your group discussion, and it is acceptable to disagree with your colleagues. I am amazed at how many group discussions I watch where everyone nods in approval at everything that is said. The "Stepford Wives" version of the group discussion is not necessarily the best group discussion. If you do not agree, say so, but do so in a way that shows that you respect your colleague and value their contribution.

- *That is an interesting point, but I'm not sure that it can necessarily be generalised.*
- *I'm not sure I am comfortable with your suggestion to make sick children sing in order to entertain the waiting room.*

It is rare for a conflict to escalate, particularly in an exam situation where everyone is being extremely careful. Any escalation is unacceptable and should be avoided if at all possible.

<u>You</u>
If you find yourself in the middle of an argument, back down graciously. Think about the TEAM rather than your own pride.

- *I'm sorry. I was getting a little overexcited then.*
- *I think I need to take a step back. What do you think of the issue, George?*

<u>Another candidate</u>

- *Can I interrupt you two for a second? I'd like to move on to…*
- *You are both very passionate about this issue. I'm not sure we can reach a conclusion today. Shall we move on?*

4 – Recurrent theme – going round in circles

If you find that the group is going over the same ground again and again, or has gone way off topic, you should attempt to bring the focus of the

discussion back to the brief again to ensure that you cover all the points required.

- *This is really interesting, but I am not sure whether, strictly speaking, it relates to the question that we are trying to answer.*
- *I'm sorry. I think I'm a little lost. Can we recap?*
- *I'd like to take another look at the brief if that is ok with everyone as I'm not sure we've covered all the points yet.*

5 – Silences

Silences can occur for a number of reasons, most commonly when the group is running out of ideas. Most assessment centres will have scenarios that easily fill the allotted time but, if you find yourself in this situation, try summarising or referring back to the brief to check that you have covered everything.

If you believe that you have finished your discussion ahead of time, you can always draw the meeting to a close early. If this happens within 5 minutes of the start of the discussion, I would strongly suggest that you have missed something, but, if you are 15 minutes into the discussion, then it may be justified to stop. In any case, it is always worth spending the last few minutes summarising the key points that you have discussed.

- *Just before we finish would anyone like to summarise?*
- *Can I make sure we have covered all the relevant points by referring back to the brief and summarising our discussion?*

6 – Too little time

This is far more likely to happen than finishing early. This is why it is crucial that one of the candidates monitors the time. When you have 5 minutes to go, you need to ensure that you start to conclude your discussion by referring back to the brief and summarising, ensuring that you have answered the whole question that was posed to you.

- *With only 5 minutes left, can we list the key issues?*
- *Can we start to draw this to a close as we only have 5 minutes left?*
- *Looking at the brief, we have still not answered the question and made our final decision. Based on our discussion and with only 5 minutes left, shall we have a vote?*

How to finish

Ideally, you would summarise the case in the final few minutes, ensure that you have answered the question and then draw the meeting to a natural close.

- *I think we've covered everything that we need to, is everyone happy with the final decision?*
- *Does anyone have anything else to add? Shall we draw the meeting to a close? Does everyone agree?*

If you are running out of time, try to have some kind of conclusion at the end.

- *We seem to have run out of time. We have about 30 seconds left. Is everyone happy with the discussion today?*

The other approach is to set up a follow-up meeting.

- *We didn't manage to discuss everything today. Perhaps we could set up another meeting to finish things off?*

Whatever happens within your group, once you are told by the assessors that you are out of time, stop talking and leave the room as directed.

Assessment criteria

The group discussion will be testing your communication skills, your ability to work in a team, your ability to problem solve, your time management and ability to work under pressure. It may also test your organisational skills if the task is to "organise a meeting" or "set up a service"; your professional integrity if the task is to "discuss a failing colleague" or "complaint"; and it may even test your probity if the task is relating to a financial matter or conflict of interest case.

The criteria used to score candidates will include many, if not all, of the following:

1 – Communication

Was the candidate clear and concise?
Did the candidate present their ideas in a structured manner?
Was the candidate able to explain the issues and their thoughts in a simple manner, easily understood by all other team members?
Did the candidate interact well with all other team members?
Did the candidate show respect for their colleagues by listening?
Did the candidate avoid confrontation?

2 – Participation

Did the candidate participate?
Was the candidate constructive?
Did the candidate ensure that their ideas could be heard when relevant?
Were the candidate's ideas confidently and coherently presented?

3 – Teamwork

Did the candidate work as a team?
Was the candidate aware of the other members of the team?
Did the candidate do anything to ease difficulties for other members?
Did the candidate actively encourage others to participate?
Did the candidate adapt their role to the needs of the group?
Did the candidate lead? How good were their leadership skills?
Did the candidate facilitate? How good were their facilitation skills?
Did the candidate support and respect the other members of their team?

4 – Time management

Did the candidate work towards ensuring that each member of the group had an equal share of the time?
Did the candidate help in overall time management?
If the candidate was involved in time management was this detrimental to their involvement in the group?
Did the candidate play a role in ensuring that the conversation remained focused on the question asked?
Did the candidate play a role in ensuring that the discussion progressed in a timely fashion?

5 – Problem solving & Interaction with others

Did the candidate contribute to solving the problem?
Did the candidate think laterally?
Was the candidate able to adapt their approach?
Was the candidate flexible to other people's ideas?
Did the candidate take on-board other people's ideas and integrate them?
If there was a disagreement in ideas, was this handled without confrontation?

6 – Overall impression

Did the other members of the team respond to the candidate?
Was the discussion productive?
Did the candidate answer the whole question?
Did the discussion lead to a natural end point?
Was there follow-up planned of any outstanding issues?

7 – Body language and voice

Did the candidate maintain eye contact?
Was their body language appropriate?
Was the candidate relaxed/ anxious/ irritated?
Could the team hear the candidate?
Was the candidate articulate?

The future

There are many ways to assess your teamwork and communication skills. Who knows... perhaps, in the future, the group discussion could include a station where the four candidates have to build a tower or complete a jigsaw puzzle – such tasks are common nature in business interviews. Whatever is being thrown at you, the principles are the same:

- Be honest.
- Communicate well.
- Respect your team and know your role.
- Adapt and be flexible.
- Manage your time.

How to prepare for the day

Practise; practise; practise. You can start right now to introduce some of the skills into your work and home life. Try watching colleagues in meetings. Who takes on which roles? Which meetings are successful? Why are they successful? Which colleagues make good team members? Why? What are they doing? How are they successful?

Practicing the techniques at work and observing others is only one step. Use the group discussion examples in the book to get together with colleagues or friends that you trust and play them out. You are unlikely to improve by just reading the examples. Remember the driving test? No one can pass by just reading the Highway Code. You need to be in a car and in the driving seat.

The gold standard, once again, is to find a reputable and well-respected course that will allow you to practise with trained observers/ tutors. Make sure it has a focus on the group discussion and has a small number of candidates. Listen to the feedback and learn from the other participants. See what works well and what doesn't. Use everything that you can to improve.

Figure 7. Summary of proposed assessment criteria for group discussions

Communication
- Clear
- Concise
- Uses appropriate language

- Interactive
- Respectful and listening
- Avoids confrontations

Participation
- Actively engages
- Constructive
- Makes self heard

- Assertive
- Confident
- Coherent

Teamwork
- Works with the team
- Shows awareness of others
- Smoothes difficulties with other colleagues
- Encourages others to participate

- Supports and respects others
- Adapts to the needs of the group
- Shows leadership whenever appropriate
- Facilitates the discussion whenever appropriate

Time management
- Played role in ensuring good time management

Problem solving
- Contributes to the resolution of the problem
- Thinks laterally

- Adaptable
- Receptive to other ideas
- Handles conflict well

Overall impression
- Good response from other candidates
- Productive discussion

- General question answered
- Follow-up and forward planning dealt with

Body language and voice
- Good eye contact
- Good body language
- Appropriate attitude

- Appropriate volume of voice
- Articulate and clear

Section 4

Group Discussion
Practice Scenarios

How to use this section

The best way to prepare for the selection centre is to step into the driving seat and have a go. This section contains examples of group discussions based on the most common type of scenarios seen at the selection centres. If you simply read through the section you will pick up some information but you will gain so much more by playing them out. To do this effectively you need at least four people, preferably five. Spend approximately 30 minutes per group discussion. Unless stated otherwise, your time should be split as follows:

Figure 8. Suggested time for each group discussion

5 minutes	The candidates read their brief
15 minutes	Group discussion
10 minutes	Feedback / debrief

Each group discussion has a group brief. It is followed by a discussion of the important information that should have been covered and a suggested structure for the group discussion. This structure cannot be enforced in a group and is merely intended to show you a possible approach that would attract a high score. When you are practicing, try using the headings described in the previous section to see how easy it is and if you think it helps the overall discussion. Try adapting the suggested ideas and develop your own rather than simply regurgitating what is written.

How to run a group discussion

There are hopefully four or five of you. One person should be nominated as your observer. If more than one of you is sitting the Stage 3 assessment, you will ideally need one observer per candidate to ensure that you receive personal and specific feedback but, if this is not possible, you can obviously try to run the group discussions with one observer for everyone.

Instructions for the observer

Make notes as the discussion progresses based on the *Summary of proposed assessment criteria for the group discussion* (see p.122). The feedback given should be honest, structured, clear and objective. When you first start to practise the observer may want to give a sign to state that there are only 5

minutes remaining. As you get nearer to the assessment day, leave it up to the group to manage their own time to make it more realistic but stop them if they run over time as would happen on the day.

Escape

Try to stay focused and "in the group" as you practise. The first few times may feel odd and you may want to set up a sign allowing people to come out of the discussion. This may be something as simple as raising your hand. You will not be able to take "time out" on the day so start to work out ways of staying in the group discussion and overcoming your difficulties as you will have to do in the assessment itself.

Feedback / debrief

After the discussion is finished it is important to complete the exercise by debriefing. Try answering the following questions as a way to start your feedback. Once this is completed, look at the discussion in the book and see how you compared.

Initial feedback questions

- Did you answer the question?
- Did everyone say something in the discussion?
- Ask each person how they felt. Did they feel listened to? Did they feel that they made a contribution to the discussion?
- Ask the observer to compare their impressions. Did they match the group's opinion?

As you practise you will develop your own style of feedback and discussion. Remember that the feedback is supposed to help you improve. It is not criticism and, if that is how it feels, try working with other people or try a course. Remember, if everyone is saying the same thing it is likely to be an accurate and fair comment. Listen and try to improve.

Rerunning

It is often useful, once you have read the feedback, to rerun part of the discussion either straight away or on another day to try out the suggested approaches in the book.

ISCMEDICAL
Interview Skills Consulting

Important Note

In order to help you practise the following group discussions, you may wish to photocopy the relevant candidates' briefs so that everyone in your group has a copy of the brief in front of them.

We have laid the book out easily so that the information for each participant holds on one single A4 sheet.

Opposite each candidate brief, you will find a space where you can make your preparatory notes. Feel free to use all the space provided but do not exceed the limits imposed.

On the day of the exam, you will often have a limited supply of paper on which to make notes. Often, you may only be permitted to use the A4 sheet on which your brief is printed.

Group Discussion
Scenario 1

Simple

GROUP DISCUSSION 1

Candidates' brief

All four candidates have the same brief.

You are working in General Practice and all four candidates are at the same level of SHO/FY2 doctors. You are about to start your weekly practice meeting but unfortunately none of the partners or the practice manager is available. The partners have asked you to start the meeting without them.

The first item on the agenda and the only one you need to cover during this meeting is regarding a patient called Mr Dalgin.

One of your colleagues (John, who is <u>not</u> present at the meeting) has twice been called to see this elderly patient (Mr Dalgin) in his own home. Mr Dalgin's health has gradually deteriorated over the last 2 years since the death of his wife and he has recently been diagnosed with a chest infection. He lives alone.

At the first visit, Mr Dalgin gave your colleague a box of chocolates to thank him for making the effort to visit him.

At the second visit today, your colleague confirmed the resolution of his chest infection and made no further plans to see him. As your colleague was leaving the house, Mr Dalgin said that he didn't have any chocolates to give but handed your colleague £50 in cash.

Your colleague has mentioned this to you in passing over coffee.

Discuss the issues involved.

──────────── **END OF THE BRIEF**────────────

GROUP DISCUSSION 1

Comments & Guidance

Read the brief

Did you spend the full 5 minutes reading the brief? It is worth giving yourself the full length of time that you will get on the day to help you appreciate how much preparation time you have. Read it and read it again.

Use the 5 minutes to make some notes.

What is this case about?

This question is looking at a probity issue. Make sure that you have read the GMC's *Good Medical Practice* before you attend the selection centre. This will help you address most of the issues raised.

Issues to cover

1 – Fact finding
It is always important in any case to get the official facts. The doctor in question is not present. It would be good practice to set up a meeting with him to find out exactly what happened. Did he try to refuse the gift? Did the patient insist? Was anything said about the future?

2 – The GMC guidance
The GMC's *Good Medical Practice* states:

> *You are not allowed to encourage patients to lend, give or bequeath money or gifts that will directly or indirectly benefit you.*

Source: GMC *Good Medical Practice* (2006) 72b

In this particular case, there is no apparent issue of pressure having been applied, but this is an issue that may need to be discussed.

3 – Local policy and guidelines

Your local Trust may have issued guidelines about the receipt of gifts from patients and other third parties such as drug reps. It may be worth looking at this. Some PCTs/ NHS Trusts have an arbitrary upper level for the value of the gift that you are allowed to receive. For example, a particular Trust may rule that all gifts up to a value of £20 can be accepted, regardless of the form in which they are given. Another Trust may rule that gifts may be accepted up to a value of £50 if they are given in kind, but that cash and vouchers must never be accepted.

4 – Our own opinion

Most people will feel comfortable accepting boxes of chocolates or sweets; indeed on many hospital wards, it is almost part of the discharge procedure to hand over a box of chocolate. Generic gifts like this that can be shared amongst the whole team happen every day.

When it comes to receiving cash, this often generates a different feeling, particularly in this case where the patient is elderly and lives alone. How can the patient afford it? Should we take cash? What will our colleagues think? Is it ethical?

What would the cut-off be for you? Nothing? £10? £50? £100? Where do we draw the line?

5 – The doctor-patient relationship

It is important to accept that some patients like giving gifts to their doctor as a sign of thanks, particularly if they have received good care. There are some ethnic groups who enjoy giving gifts, expect the doctor to take it and would be offended if the doctor refused. In such cases, a compromise needs to be reached. We need to ensure that we are maintaining a good working relationship with our patients without contradicting our personal or professional boundaries. By bluntly refusing the gift, we may offend our patient. By accepting it, we may be breaking our personal and professional beliefs and ethics

6 – *Options for the gift and money*

The chocolates can be shared between the team and most people will find this acceptable. The money is slightly different.

<u>Should we keep it for ourselves?</u>
I personally would not advocate this, although I do know some doctors who would. If you are tempted to keep the money, ensure that you are transparent and inform your practice manager, Consultant or GP partner. It is also worth writing to the patient thanking them for the donation. A copy of this letter can then be filed in the notes ensuring that there is an audit trail.

<u>Should we donate it to the practice?</u>
There are two ways of doing this:

a. We can buy things for the practice such as tea, coffee, biscuits and chocolate for the whole team to enjoy. This again will allow us to thank the patient on behalf of the whole team. After all, it was the receptionists who took the call to make the home visits; the nurses and other doctors have looked after him in the past.

b. The alternative is to give the money to the practice manager who will add it to the practice fund. There may be a party or night out planned. Perhaps the money could be donated to that? Once again, we should acknowledge the patient and thank them on behalf of the whole team.

<u>Should we donate it to a charity?</u>
There are many local and national charities that would benefit from the money. Informing the patient and thanking them on behalf of the charity would be advised.

7 – *The escalation of the gift*

Why has the patient increased the value of the gift? Did he think that he had to pay? Did he think that he would not get the standard of care if he didn't pay for it?

It is important to ensure that the patient does not feel that he has to continue to pay. Once a patient feels that their care is being influenced by

giving gifts, we are then as doctors encouraging them – albeit indirectly – to continue this practice.

You need to ensure that someone contacts the patient to ensure that he understands the gift was appreciated but that, in future, the practice would prefer that the patient did not give money as it is unnecessary and that the patient's care will still continue with or without gifts.

8 – *The future*

One thing to think about is discussing a future policy for gifts and donations. If the practice does not have a local policy you could suggest setting one up. This could start with a prospective study or audit of all gifts received.

9 – *Documentation and reporting*

Clarity of written and verbal reporting should be raised and confirmed. It is always important to document everything that happens with our patients. Where would you suggest documenting cases such as this? The clinical notes? A practice "donation book"? I would advocate always keeping a personal record of any gift received. This can then be discussed openly at your appraisal at the end of the year.

It is always useful to try to talk about as many appropriate NHS issues as you can. This could include audit, appraisal, probity, professional guidance and clinical governance amongst others in this case. There may be extra points waiting to be scored!

Conclusion

This scenario covers a key topic that is often covered in GP selection. It is not exhaustive and you may have had many other ideas. Make sure that you look back at the proposed assessment criteria. Remember that the group discussion station is more about HOW you discuss the issues (i.e. how you contribute, support and respect others) than WHAT you say.

Group Discussion
Scenario 2

Extended Simple
With Presentation

GROUP DISCUSSION 2

Candidates' brief

All candidates have the same brief.

You are four junior doctors at the same level (SHO/FY2). You are attending your hospital's ethics committee meeting and have been asked to discuss one of the cases in advance to present to the committee. You need to make a decision to put before the committee of Consultants. You will each individually be asked to report to one Consultant at the end of the 20 minutes to inform them of the group's decision.

The case

Amy Romberg is a 15-year-old girl who was born with bilateral talipes (club feet). This is a congenital abnormality resulting in a deformity of the feet. The orthopaedic surgeons have approached the ethics committee for advice as they would like to proceed with surgical correction in the form of an ankle fusion but have problems as the parents have refused to allow them to proceed.

You need to decide whether Amy can have the surgery.

To help you in your decision, you are being given evidence presented by the patient, the parents, the surgeon and the teacher.

You are given 10 minutes to review the evidence before proceeding with the discussion (20 minutes).

The evidence

Amy's evidence

I am 15. I was born with an abnormality of both my feet. They tried physiotherapy when I was a baby, but I ended up having two operations. When I was 11 my feet deteriorated and I had to stop doing the sports that I loved and ended up wearing leg splints. The splints keep my ankles in a fixed position but I still get a lot of pain. I also get bullied at school. I have seen physiotherapists and surgeons at the hospital who all think it would benefit me to have this operation to fuse my ankles to help with the pain. I have waited for 3 years, as they needed to be sure that my bones had stopped growing. I understand what is going to happen, know about the risks and would like to go ahead as soon as I can.

The parents' evidence

We have one daughter called Amy. She is an only child. She was born with bilateral club feet and throughout her life we have been back and forth to hospitals and physiotherapists. She had two major operations on her feet as a baby and has done really well over the last few years. The last surgeon she saw said that, as her feet had stopped growing, he could do an operation to fuse her ankle and foot bones to try and help with the pain. We have been told it is not 100% effective but will hopefully help with her pain. This is not a life-saving operation. If Amy wears her leg splints every day she doesn't get the pain. She has started trying to wear girly footwear that her splints will not fit in. This is making things worse. We are not prepared to put Amy's life at risk for a cosmetic procedure. We refuse to consent.

>>>> **Brief continues on the next page** >>>>

The teacher's evidence

(Amy and her parents have consented to her teacher having information about her case.)

I have been teaching Amy for 4 years. She is a very sensible and bright girl. She has suffered terribly over the last 2 years with bullying. We have tried to stop this at the school and things are better, but Amy is certain that things will improve further if her feet are fixed and she no longer has to wear her splints. She has discussed the operation with me and appears to know the risks involved. I understand that it will take a while to heal. Her GCSE year is next year and it is important that she is fit for that.

The surgeon's evidence

Amy has bilateral severe talipes. Her feet will not improve and, although wearing leg splints has helped to control her pain, this requires regular hospital visits and the splints are unsightly. Her bones have all now finished growing with fused growth plates and so this would be the time to have the surgery. An ankle fusion will help cosmetically as she will no longer need to wear her splints but will leave her with no movement in the ankles. It is a significant operation, but is routine in our department and I have total faith in her full recovery. If we perform the procedure now she will be fully recovered in time for her exams next year. There is no reason why she cannot study whilst her feet are recovering. I have assessed Amy and have found her to be bright and fully competent to make her own decisions.

————————————————— **END OF THE BRIEF**—————————————————

Use this box to make your preparatory notes

GROUP DISCUSSION 2

Comments & Guidance

Read the brief

Did you spend the full 10 minutes reading the brief? It is worth giving yourself the full length of time that you will get on the day to help you appreciate how much preparation time you have. In this case, where the candidate brief is long and complicated, you may not have enough time to fully think through everything. If you have time, read it and read it again until you are happy.

If you can, use the 10 minutes to make some notes. Remember what they are assessing you on. Many points are awarded on HOW you discuss the case and they are not all focused on WHAT you say.

You may know very little, if anything, about congenital talipes and orthopaedic surgery. It does not matter. Be honest. Perhaps one way of starting the discussion is to state this.

- *I have to be honest and tell you that I know very little about the medicine involved in this case. Can anyone fill in any gaps?*
- *Shall we concentrate on the ethical issues in this case rather than the surgery itself?*

What is this case about?

The main issues in this case are ethics and consent. Read the GMC's and other guidelines for full factual information on these subjects.

Important information to consider

1 – Ethical principles

The four basic ethical principles in medicine are:

- **AUTONOMY**
  This is based on the Greek word autonomia – the freedom to live by one's own laws. In modern medicine it forms the basis of informed consent. Allow the patient to choose.

  If a patient is deemed to be competent, they are able to undertake informed consent and can therefore choose if they want to have the offered treatment or not.

  Competence/ capacity: the patient understands the pros and cons of proceeding with the treatment; they understand the pros and cons of not proceeding with the treatment; can retain that information and explain it to others.

- **BENEFICENCE**
  First do good. This comes before non-maleficence for a reason.

- **NON-MALEFICENCE**
  Do no harm.

- **JUSTICE**
  Fairness. All cases should be treated the same independently of sex, race, age, religion, size, etc.

2 – Consent

The official age of consent is 16. Above this age anyone who is competent and therefore has capacity can accept or refuse treatment.

Below the age of 16 the law is different dependent on whether you are in England/ Wales or Scotland. Check your local guidelines.

Under "Gillick competence", now called "Fraser guidelines", if a child under 16 is competent (and therefore has capacity) then he can consent to treatment

without parental consent. However, as a doctor, you have a duty to discuss with the child whether parental involvement should be considered.

The Fraser ruling was initially passed in relation to prescribing the oral contraceptive pill but can be used for any treatment or procedure. It is most relevant for older teenagers since, below the age of 12, patients are unlikely to be competent. It is important to consider though that each child is different and should be judged individually.

In England and Wales, if a child under 16 refused to consent for treatment that is thought to be in their best interest, then parental consent can override the child's decision. In Scotland, however, a child under 16 is allowed to refuse to give consent.

Issues to cover

1 – Fact finding

It is always important in any case to get the official facts. We have all the information in front of us.

In favour of the treatment
The child is 15, competent and wants the procedure. The surgeon feels that the operation is in her best interest. She has the support of a responsible adult in the form of a teacher.

Against the treatment
The parents do not feel that it is necessary.

What information would be helpful? There are some facts missing:

- Have we had a joint meeting with all parties to try to resolve the issues?
- Who will support Amy when she is post-op? Will she go home?
- How soon are her exams? Will she be fully recovered before they start? Will she lose any important time from school?
- Have we consulted the medical defence unions (MDU / MPS)?
- Have we consulted the hospital legal team?

2 – The GMC guidance as above

When dealing with competent teenagers, it is important that they are involved in the discussion whatever the consent issues. The GMC advises us to encourage all children to talk to, and get support from, their parents or guardians. In an ideal situation, we would have an open discussion with the parents and Amy to attempt to resolve any differences with both parties present. This is not always possible.

3 – Our own opinion

How do we feel about this case? Our own beliefs will influence our final decision even if we try to be completely impartial.

4 – School

How important do we feel Amy's final year at school is? Could increased support at school and zero tolerance against bullying help Amy to complete her exams without needing the surgery? Perhaps an offer of an educational assembly at school on talipes and the need for Amy to wear splints would help. Would a change of school help?

5 – Options

a. Agree that Amy is competent and allow the procedure to happen without mum and dad consenting.

b. Agree that Amy is competent but, since it is a big operation, suggest that it can only go ahead if mum and dad support the decision. You could offer group meetings and family therapy/ support to aid this decision.

c. Ignore the Fraser ruling and refuse to allow the procedure unless mum and dad support the decision and sign the consent form.

d. Postpone making a decision until more information is received.

e. Postpone the procedure for a year. Amy is 15 and will not need parental support once she is 16. At the age of 16, her exams will also be completed and she would have longer to recover.

There is no right or wrong answer, but the brief clearly states that you need to make a decision as a team to present to the Consultants. Sitting on the fence and avoiding a decision may cost you valuable points. Whatever decision the group came to should be unanimous and justified by the facts.

6 – The future

These types of cases often present themselves. Is there a local policy on under-16s and consent without parental support? If not, you could suggest that a policy is written. You could suggest an audit of other cases to see how common it is and the difficulties encountered. Implement your policy and see if things have improved. Reaudit.

7 – Documentation and reporting

Clarity of written and verbal reporting should be raised and confirmed. It is always important to document everything that happens with our patients. In this case, all conversations with mum and dad, the teacher and Amy should be recorded. Advice from the medical defence unions (MDU / MPS) and hospital lawyers should also be recorded.

8 – The presentation

Did you leave enough time in your discussion to make a group decision? Did you agree with the overall group decision?

In presenting the ideas, always think about who you are presenting to. In this case it is a Consultant. The terminology you use will therefore be medically and ethically based. Be prepared to give the overall decision and to justify it. You may need to make a few notes during the discussion for the presentation to ensure that you cover all the salient points.

Be prepared to be asked questions about why the group came to the decision that it did.

Remember that the assessor will have heard the whole discussion and will know if you are telling the truth or not.

It is always useful to try to talk about audit, appraisal, probity, professional guidance and clinical governance amongst others (if indicated) in the group discussion. There may be extra points waiting to be scored!

Conclusion

This covers two important topics that could be covered during a group discussion of this kind. It is not exhaustive and you may have had many other ideas.

Make sure that you look back at the proposed assessment criteria. Remember that this section is more about HOW you discuss the issues raised both in terms of your own contribution and in supporting and respecting your team rather than WHAT you say?

Group Discussion Scenario 3

Extended Complicated

GROUP DISCUSSION 3

Candidates' briefs

Each candidate will see a different brief. These are covered over four separate pages to help run the practice scenario without each candidate seeing the whole brief. Before you go any further, get each participant to choose a number and ensure that they read their brief only.

BRIEF FOR CANDIDATE 1

You are an SHO/ FY2 doctor and are attending your hospital's significant event meeting. There has been a complaint from a bereaved family regarding the care of their deceased relative. You are asked to form a subcommittee with three other doctors to discuss the case and need to decide what, if any, action should be taken. Each member of the subcommittee has a different report to consider.

Extract from the Consultant cardiologist's report

Edna had mild ischaemic heart disease and was admitted for routine coronary angiography. Unfortunately, during the angiogram, we punctured the posterior aspect of her femoral artery from which she bled. She dropped her blood pressure to 60/40 during the procedure, which was immediately halted, and she was resuscitated with fluids with good effect. We sent off an FBC and "group and save" sample and monitored her in the angiography suite for 2 hours. The suite closed at 17:00 and so we returned her to the ward at 16:30 with instructions for a blood transfusion to be arranged when the FBC result came back.

I left the hospital at 17:00. When I returned in the morning I heard about the arrest and her death.

———————————— END OF CANDIDATE 1 BRIEF ————————————

Use this box to make your preparatory notes (Candidate 1)

BRIEF FOR CANDIDATE 2

You are an SHO / FY2 doctor and are attending your hospital's significant event meeting. There has been a complaint from a bereaved family regarding the care of their deceased relative. You are asked to form a subcommittee with three other doctors to discuss the case and need to decide what, if any, action should be taken. Each member of the subcommittee has a different report to consider.

Extract from the family's complaint letter

Edna was a 74-year-old lady who was living independently in a warden-controlled flat. She had a good social life and was able to walk unaided. She had, over the last 2 years, suffered with slight angina and was due to have a routine angiogram. We were told she would be home the same day.

Things went wrong and she suffered a bleed into her groin from her artery. This was from the puncture site where the doctor had put a catheter to pass up into her heart. We understand that these things can happen but she bled a great deal and a decision was made to treat her conservatively with blood transfusions. She never received that blood transfusion. We understand that a Consultant made the decision but no one chased the result of her full blood count and no one gave her the fluids or blood that she needed.

The family visited her that evening and we realised something was wrong. We informed the nurses on four occasions that we thought she was sick and the nurses looked at her and took her blood pressure but did nothing.

Edna got paler and paler and, in front of our eyes, stopped breathing. We called for the nurses and there was a cardiac arrest call made. They tried to resuscitate her but were unable to. She died.

We understand that her blood count was 4 when it was measured at the arrest. Before the angiogram it was 12.

———————————— **END OF CANDIDATE 2 BRIEF**————————————

Use this box to make your preparatory notes (Candidate 2)

BRIEF FOR CANDIDATE 3

You are an SHO/ FY2 doctor and are attending your hospital's significant event meeting. There has been a complaint from a bereaved family regarding the care of their deceased relative. You are asked to form a subcommittee with three other doctors to discuss the case and need to decide what, if any, action should be taken. Each member of the subcommittee has a different report to consider.

Extract from the nurse's report

Edna was returned to our ward from the cardiology department at 16:30. We were told that there had been a complication and that she had bled from her femoral artery after the procedure. They had kept her in recovery in the angiography suite for 2 hours and her blood pressure and pulse were stable. The angiography suite closed at 17:00 and this was a normal procedure to return her to the ward.

The ward was very busy with one trained and four other nurses on duty. We were looking after 28 patients. Our second trained nurse had called in sick. Edna appeared stable and on arrival her observations were stable.

The family came to visit shortly after she arrived on the ward and on four occasions over an hour informed the auxiliary nurses that they were worried. Each time the nurse took her routine observations. No abnormality was reported to the nurse in charge but on the fourth time, due to the family anxiety, the ward staff attempted to contact the on-call doctor. The doctor did not respond to multiple bleeps.

As the trained nurse on duty I only saw Edna as she arrived on the ward. The next time I saw her was after the arrest call had been made. As the bell sounded I immediately stopped what I was doing and ran to Edna's bedside. The resuscitation was unsuccessful. Edna died at 18:00.

We did report at the time that the on-call doctor whom we tried to bleep earlier attended the arrest and smelt of alcohol.

———————————— **END OF CANDIDATE 3 BRIEF**————————————

BRIEF FOR CANDIDATE 4

You are an SHO/ FY2 doctor and are attending your hospital's significant event meeting. There has been a complaint from a bereaved family regarding the care of their deceased relative. You are asked to form a subcommittee with three other doctors to discuss the case and need to decide what, if any, action should be taken. Each member of the subcommittee has a different report to consider.

Extract from the on-call doctor's report

I was the on-call doctor on the day that Edna died. I started work at 08:00 and was due to finish at 20:00. I had been busy all day and stopped to get a drink at 17:25. This was the first time I had sat down all day. I had a list of things to do and my bleep did not stop ringing. At 17:40 the arrest call went out and I immediately ran to the arrest.

A 74-year-old woman post cardiac angiography, which was complicated by a bleed, had arrested. She had no output and no spontaneous respiratory effort. We tried to resuscitate with fluids and multiple cycles of cardiopulmonary resuscitation (CPR) including the use of the defibrillator whilst waiting for blood to arrive from the blood bank. The urgent FBC that we sent to the lab came back at 4.2 and, despite the blood arriving quickly, we were unable to save her. She died at 18:00.

————————————— **END OF CANDIDATE 4 BRIEF**—————————————

Use this box to make your preparatory notes (Candidate 4)

GROUP DISCUSSION 3

Comments & Guidance

Read the brief

Did you spend the full 5 minutes reading the brief? It is worth giving yourself the full length of time that you will get on the day to help you appreciate how much preparation time you have. Read it and read it again.

The important thing to remember about this type of group discussion is that each candidate has different information. You need to ensure that everyone had time to talk through all the issues raised in their brief otherwise you will never be able to reach a sensible and concerted decision. Have a look at all of the briefs again. Did you have time to discuss all of the information on the sheets?

If you find that there is some information that you didn't have time to talk about, think about why. What went wrong? Was it your time management as a group? Was there a dominant member of the group who took over? Was there simply too much information to cover?

Try to think about what you could have done differently. Try rerunning the discussion using some of the alternatives to see if the discussion runs differently. Try running the discussion with a different group of people. Changing the dynamics of a group by adding in different people will change the whole exercise.

During your 5 minutes of preparation at the beginning, use the time to make some notes. Think about what you are about to be assessed on.

What is this case about?

This question is based on the complaints procedure, but also about an underperforming colleague. Did you pick up on the sentence in the nurse's brief about the doctor on call "smelling of alcohol"?

Reporting underperforming colleagues is a key aspect in the GMC's *Good Medical Practice*. Ensure that you read it from cover to cover before you attend the selection centre. This will help you address most of the issues raised.

Issues to cover

The important issues are:

1 – A complaint that needs investigation and appropriate response

> Most complaints in the NHS relate to communication issues. In this case something clearly went wrong and it is important to cover in your discussion the steps that went wrong in Edna's care. She did not receive her blood transfusion that may have saved her life by preventing the arrest. We need to look at all sides of the story to work out why that happened and a full investigation needs to be completed.
>
> There are several factors contributing to the mistake. This includes:
>
> - **Facilities** (in the form of the angiography suite closing at 17:00).
>
> - **Personnel** (understaffed wards, the Consultant leaving at 17:00, an overworked junior doctor).
>
> - **Time** issues relating to breaks for the junior doctor and end of the day management/ handover from the angiography suite to the ward.
>
> - **Funding** issues. If more money were available would there have been an HDU bed? Would the hospital have had agency nursing staff to cover the sick nurse?
>
> The GMC's *Good Medical Practice* covers the essential behaviour when faced with a complaint and dealing with relatives after a patient has died. Read the whole booklet before your selection centre assessment.

ISCMEDICAL
Interview Skills Consulting

It is always important to acknowledge a complaint, to investigate and to respond quickly and efficiently. Take a look at your local policies about complaints. It is essential that an apology be given in cases where things have gone wrong. Many doctors are worried that by apologising they may be admitting a wrongdoing, thereby opening themselves up to litigation. This is not the case. Many patients and relatives just want to know the truth and have someone say "I'm sorry". Communication in this way may actually avoid litigation cases.

How did you, as a group, decide to communicate with the family? By letter? An open meeting? Every Trust now has a Patient Advice and Liaison Service (PALS). PALS is run by patient advocates and is a useful start when communicating about complaints.

Other people who could be involved are the chaplaincy team if Edna or her family are religious or the hospital bereavement officers who are trained to deal with grieving families.

2 – An understaffed ward

Discussion about the ward's staffing is important. Why was there only one trained nurse on duty? What facilities does the hospital have for covering staff who call in sick? You could suggest an audit of staffing levels or setting up a local policy to prevent this situation arising again.

3 – The angiography suite closing early and patient being moved

Was it appropriate to move Edna when they did? If an angiography suite closes, is that a good enough reason to move a patient? What could have been done differently? Could paying the staff overtime to look after a patient in this situation be justified? Should Edna have been moved to an HDU or monitored more closely elsewhere?

4 – Overworked junior doctors

The junior doctor on call was very busy. They stated that they had not had a natural break in nine hours of duty. This is unacceptable. The European Working Time Directive states that doctors working a full shift pattern should have a 30-minute break for every 4 hours worked. Doctors on a partial shift pattern (as in this case) are entitled to regular short breaks and in total one quarter of the out of hours time worked.

This doctor worked from 08:00 until 20:00. If we take the normal working day as 09:00-17:00 then this doctor worked four hours of "out of hours" time. This doctor should have had at least a one-hour break. The doctor stated in their report that no breaks had been taken. This doctor was not getting the official rest during their shift and this raises concerns. Is this a safe environment for patients? Is this doctor underperforming? The whole shift pattern needs to be reviewed. Are there enough doctors? Should the shift pattern be changed to a full shift?

The nurse's statement stated that the doctor did not respond to four bleeps. The doctor stated they were taking a quick break to get a drink and their bleep repeatedly went off.

There is clearly a problem with the workload. Something would need to be put in place to help the junior doctors cope. You could suggest a diary card exercise for all doctors to look at their working patterns as a start.

5 – An underperforming colleague

This relates to the statement from the nurses that the junior doctor smelt of alcohol when they arrived at the arrest. This needs addressing and investigating.

A way to approach this would be to firstly work out the facts.

a. Recruit information by approaching the junior doctor. It may be that the doctor has a problem with alcohol and needs support. It could be that they use alcohol gel to clean their hands and that is what the nurses smelt.

b. Recruit information from the junior doctor's educational supervisor. Are there any concerns with their work or progress?

If there is any concern regarding the junior doctor or there are other reports about their drinking then the GMC guidance is to report that issue as soon as is possible whilst ensuring that the patients are not put at risk. If the doctor does have a drinking problem, you would need to:

- **Protect the patients** and allow the doctor to go home on sick leave. If the doctor in question has already seen patients, you would need to arrange for any decisions made to be reviewed.

- **Report the matter**. The GMC advises we report internally and use local policies to deal with the case. The educational supervisor would be the first person to tell, who would hopefully support the doctor and ensure that their problem is dealt with.

- **Support** the doctor. If the doctor has an alcohol problem we need to ensure that they get the support and treatment that is required. This can be from the educational supervisor, occupational health, their own GP or the confidential network of support groups specifically for doctors. There are many listed in the back of the weekly medical press.

6 – The future

You may want to discuss the setting up of a future policy for complaints and reporting colleagues. Suggest an audit. You can also cover issues of clinical governance in this case.

7 – Documentation and reporting

Clarity of written and verbal reporting should be raised and confirmed. It is always important to document everything that happens with our patients, including what happens after they have died.

It is always useful to try to talk about audit, appraisal, probity, professional guidance and clinical governance amongst others – if indicated in the group discussion. There may be extra points waiting to be scored!

Conclusion

This covers a key subject that could be covered during a group discussion of this kind. It is not exhaustive and you may have had many other ideas. Make sure that you look back at the proposed assessment criteria. Remember that this section is more about HOW you discuss the issues raised both in terms of your own contribution and in supporting and respecting your team rather than WHAT you say. Time management is also key in this case.

ISC MEDICAL
Interview Skills Consulting

Group Discussion Scenario 4

Role-orientated

GROUP DISCUSSION 4

Candidates' briefs

All candidates have the same information in their brief, but each candidate is given a different "role" to play.

Maggie is a 28-year-old woman with Down's syndrome. She lives in sheltered accommodation with other young people with disabilities and, although she is able to wash and dress herself, she needs help with most other tasks, including financial management, shopping and cooking.

Maggie has had a boyfriend for 2 years and, as the staff knew that they had started a sexual relationship, Maggie was on the contraceptive depot injection given by the practice nurse. Maggie is now 12 weeks pregnant. It is thought that her last depot injection was one week late and this is the cause. She wants to keep the baby and understands what pregnancy and children involve. She has a mental age equivalent to a 12-year-old child.

The father of the baby is her long-term boyfriend who also lives in the shelter and has cerebral palsy. He has a similar mental age and is also physically disabled. Maggie and her boyfriend have no family and have been under the care of social services for their entire life.

Roles   Candidate 1   The GP
           Candidate 2   The practice nurse
           Candidate 3   The social worker
           Candidate 4   Occupational therapist who supports Maggie at the centre during the day

The care team at the sheltered housing have suggested that they would be unable to continue to look after Maggie if she had a child. They feel that she would need 24-hour care if she kept the child and wonder if there are any other options available to them.

Discuss the options available to Maggie and her boyfriend and decide which you think would be the best option for her.
————————————— **END OF THE BRIEF**—————————————

Use this box to make your preparatory notes

GROUP DISCUSSION 4

Comments & Guidance

Read the brief

Did you spend the full 5 minutes reading the brief? It is worth giving yourself the full length of time that you will get on the day to help you appreciate how much preparation time you have. Read it and read it again.

Use the 5 minutes to make some notes. Try to remember what they are assessing you on.

s well as your communication skills and ability to interact, this case also tests your knowledge of the multidisciplinary team. It is worth making sure you know a little bit about the role of each person in a multidisciplinary team before you attend your selection centre. This would include:

- Doctor
- Nurse
- Specialist nurse
- Nurse Consultant
- District/ community nurse
- Occupational therapist
- Physiotherapist
- Speech therapist
- Pharmacist
- Social worker

- Health visitor
- Staff
- Midwife
- Patient
- Patient representatives
- Bereavement officer
- PALS
- Support staff
- Clerical
- Cleaners

This is not an exhaustive list and you may be able to think of others.

What is this case about?

This is an ethical question. Make sure that you have read the GMC's *Good Medical Practice* before you attend the selection centre. This will give you the definitive answer to many of the issues raised. The GMC will also have

guidance covering issues relating to the right to life and the right of patients with disabilities.

Issues to consider

There are several important issues to consider:

1 – Maggie and her right to choose

We know that Maggie has the mental capacity of a 12 year old. Does she have capacity? Can she make an informed choice relating to this pregnancy? Does she understand the pros and cons of going ahead with the pregnancy and also the other options available to her?

For clarification of these terms, refer to group discussion scenario 2.

To help with this decision, you could suggest that the GP sees and assesses her. You could also refer her to a learning disability specialist who could assess her capacity if it is in any doubt. Talking to the staff at the sheltered housing would also be beneficial. They say that they cannot keep Maggie if she had a child. Why is that? Is it relating to a "no children" policy or do they not believe Maggie would cope?

If Maggie is found to be competent, we need to think about the ethical principle of autonomy. With capacity, it is her right to choose and the pregnancy would have to go ahead unless a compromise could be reached with her.

If she is found not to have capacity, then Maggie's autonomy is no longer an issue and we need to then discuss the case with Maggie's named advocate.

2 – The right of the unborn child

The unborn child has no rights at all. Until a child is born, legally it has no say. This often comes as a shock to people who do not support termination of pregnancy.

3 – *Options for the pregnancy*

    a. Allow the pregnancy to go ahead if Maggie has capacity and arrange for 24-hour care for her and the child.
    b. Allow the pregnancy to go ahead and let the child be placed into foster care ensuring that Maggie has access.
    c. Allow the pregnancy to proceed but let the child be adopted.
    d. Arrange for a termination of pregnancy.

4 – *Support for Maggie*

<u>Psychological support</u>
Ensure that Maggie has support to enable her to talk through the issues involved and to help her make an informed decision if she is able to.

This could be at the home by the OT, resident counsellor or support staff.

The family planning service will always have a counsellor attached to their service. The "young persons" counsellor may be the best person to talk to if Maggie has the mental age of a 12 year old.

The practice nurse has met Maggie several times to give her the depot injection. The nurse may have a good relationship with her and be able to support and counsel her.

The social services may have counselling services available.

Whether Maggie has a termination or goes ahead with the pregnancy, she is going to need significant psychological support at all stages.

<u>Financial support</u>
Maggie is in full-time accommodation and will be exclusively supported by social services and the benefit system. If the pregnancy did go ahead, financial support would be essential. Social workers are often best placed to investigate this type of support.

<u>Social support</u>
The staff in the home know Maggie well and the OT in particular is likely to know about Maggie's social situation and set-up. Social services and OT may have alternative options of a social support network.

Physical support
If Maggie goes ahead with the pregnancy she will need to ensure that her physical health is good. This can be monitored by the GP, practice nurse and carers in the home. The community and hospital midwives in addition to the medical team would play an important role.

5 – Facilities

If the pregnancy went ahead, what are the options and what facilities are available?

If Maggie keeps the child
- 24-hour supported accommodation.
- A family home. Could Maggie and the baby be "fostered"?
- Maggie could stay where she is, with increased support in the home.

If Maggie does not keep the child
- Maggie could stay where she is and the baby could be placed elsewhere with or without Maggie visiting. This would involve foster care or adoption.
- Maggie could stay where she is and have a termination of pregnancy.

6 – Funding

Social services would have to pay for all the above options. The termination of pregnancy would be performed on the NHS.

7 – Depot injection

Why did Maggie get pregnant whilst on depot? It would be worth assessing her notes to ensure that she did have the correct dose of depot at the correct time. The brief states that her injection was given too late. Is this correct? If there was an issue with the timing of the depot, the practice would need to investigate this. Why was it given late?

You could suggest that an audit is carried out to look at all women in the practice on the depot injection. What steps can you put in place for the future to ensure that no other injection is given late?

Has the issue of safe sex, contraception and sexually transmitted diseases been discussed?

8 – Personal feelings

When dealing with the potential option of termination of pregnancy many of us will have our own deep-seated beliefs either in favour or against the procedure. These feelings and opinions are acceptable.

If we disagree with any issue or treatment in medicine we are allowed to refuse to give that treatment as long as we ensure that the patient is not distressed or influenced by our belief and that we offer an alternative practitioner who will discuss the options with them.

Was this a problem in your group discussion? How did you resolve it? What would you do if you were faced with a candidate in your assessment that refused to talk about termination of pregnancy?

9 – Decision

The brief clearly stated that, as a group, you should make a decision. This may feel like an impossible task, but did you manage it? If not, why not? What would you do differently if faced with a similar case in your assessment?

10 – Documentation and reporting

Clarity of written and verbal reporting should be raised and confirmed. It is always important to document everything that happens with our patients. Details of this meeting should be recorded in Maggie's notes.

It is always useful to try to talk about audit, appraisal, probity, professional guidance and clinical governance amongst others (where indicated) in the group discussion. There may be extra points waiting to be scored!

Conclusion

This covers a key subject that could be covered during a group discussion of this kind. It is not exhaustive and you may have had many other ideas. Make sure that you look back at the proposed assessment criteria. Remember that this section is more about HOW you discuss the issues raised both in terms of your own contribution and in supporting and respecting your team rather than WHAT you say.

Group Discussion
Scenario 5

Simple

GROUP DISCUSSION 5

Candidates' briefs

All candidates have the same brief.

You are four doctors based in hospital at the SHO/ FY2 level. You have met over lunchtime as you are concerned about one of your Registrars, who appears to be having many problems.

The Registrar was an excellent support until 2 months ago when things changed. Initially he started turning up late for work and one night, whilst he was due to be resident, covering the on-call rota, he was unavailable on his bleep for over 2 hours. When he was finally contacted he gave no reason, but just said that he "had things to do". Over the last week he has appeared dishevelled, wearing unironed clothes, and today you saw him in the drug cupboard placing medication into his pocket.

Discuss the issues.

——————————————— END OF THE BRIEF ———————————————

Use this box to make your preparatory notes

GROUP DISCUSSION 5

Comments & Guidance

Read the brief

Did you spend the full 5 minutes reading the brief? It is worth giving yourself the full length of time that you will get on the day to help you appreciate how much preparation time you have. Read it and read it again.

Use the 5 minutes to make some notes.

What is this case about?

This question is about our relationships with our colleagues and about protecting our patients. Make sure that you have read the GMC's *Good Medical Practice* before you attend the selection centre. This will help you address most of the issues raised.

Your attention will need to focus on

- **The patient**
  Good Medical Practice states that our first concern is to protect our patients and prevent them from harm.

- **Our colleague**
  Good Medical Practice states that we have a duty to support our colleagues.

- **Reporting**
  Good Medical Practice states that, if we have any concerns regarding a colleague's conduct, performance or health, we have a duty to report these concerns to an appropriate person. We are encouraged to follow local guidelines and to only report to the defence unions and GMC if we cannot resolve them by these means.

Issues to discuss

1 – Fact finding

The Registrar in question is not present at the meeting and he is the only one who knows the true facts. There are a number of reasons that could account for his behaviour in recent months and it is important to determine what is happening. It could be that his wife has just left him and he has three small children to look after at home. He may be having difficulty coping with stress or bereavement. He may have an illness (either physical or psychological). He may have started to abuse alcohol or drugs. He could be overworked or stressed as he is about to sit his part 3 postgraduate exit examination. He may be "burnt out" and be considering leaving the profession. Who knows?!

Who is best to determine this information?

You may have a good relationship with this Registrar and so could suggest that one or more of you sit with him over lunch or outside work and see if there is anything you can do to help.

Is there another Registrar who knows him well that you think he would confide in? Do any of his friends work at the hospital with him? Could you approach one of these and ask them to help?

Who is your Consultant? Could you approach them and ask them to help by explaining how concerned you are for his welfare?

Who is your educational supervisor? Could you approach them to ask for help?

2 – Support

By supporting our colleagues and working as a team we may be able to prevent this Registrar from receiving a patient complaint or from making a potentially life-threatening mistake. Once we have found out what is causing his change in behaviour there are many ways we can try to help.

a.   Offering support by listening and talking.

b. Offering suggestions of places to go for help. This may include colleagues, occupational health, his own GP or the specific doctors support networks as advertised in the medical press.

c. Offering practical solutions. If the Registrar has childcare issues, we could cover the early part of their shift to enable them to take the child to school. We could offer to swap shifts (if on the same rota) to ease the burden upon them.

d. Advising them to talk to a senior colleague for help.

3 – Patient protection

The GMC guidance states that we must act promptly to ensure that our patients are protected from colleagues that we consider to be a risk. If you have any concerns regarding patient care, your immediate response should be to protect your patient. If you are able to approach the Registrar yourself, you could suggest holding their bleep and allowing them to go home. If you are unable to approach your Registrar, you will need to report this internally by following your local guidelines. The usual route is by approaching a senior colleague and informing them of your concerns. They will then be responsible for following this to its conclusion.

People to whom you could report a colleague include:

- A senior doctor in your team (SHO, Registrar, Consultant)
- Your educational supervisor
- Your college tutor
- Occupational health physician
- A senior member of the team (specialist nurse, senior sister)
- Your junior doctor representative (this may allow you to remain anonymous)
- The clinical director.

The person you will choose will depend on the degree of your concern and your personal relationship with the colleague.

4 – Our own opinion

Whether we like it or not our own opinions and values will influence our response. The facts that we find out along the way will influence our

response. It is essential that we adhere to our local and GMC guidelines if a patient is at risk.

5 – The medication

The Registrar was witnessed taking drugs from the drug cupboard and placing them into his pocket. This needs to be followed up. Taking anything from the NHS is stealing and, in theory, you could be prosecuted.

Many NHS Trusts now have a "report your colleague" rule if you witness anyone taking anything that belongs to the NHS. Many Trusts state that "disciplinary action will be taken" in all these cases. This rule applies to envelopes and paper, patient dinners and hospital drugs.

The other thing to consider is whether the Registrar could be abusing prescription drugs. This may be the reason for his recent behaviour change. Once again, this is firstly a fact-finding approach. Perhaps the Registrar was getting drugs from the cupboard as prescribed to give to a patient.

Would it matter if the drug was paracetamol? How differently would you feel if it was diazepam or morphine? Where do we draw the line? In theory it is wrong to take any drug. Would you report him in each of the above situations?

6 – The future

If there is no clear local policy you could suggest implementing a working party to devise some local guidelines and to audit them following implementation.

7 – Documentation and reporting

Clarity of written and verbal reporting should be raised and confirmed. It is always important to document everything. Where would you suggest documenting cases such as this? Would the clinical notes be appropriate?

This type of generic problem may well be better documented by keeping an individual log of events and discussions. It is unlikely that this information will be requested but in the rare circumstance that evidence is required, for example in the case of a colleague who goes on to commit a

mistake or commits suicide, it is always easier to have your own clear notes for reference.

Conclusion

This covers a key subject that could be covered during a group discussion of this kind. It is not exhaustive and you may have had many other ideas. Make sure that you look back at the proposed assessment criteria. Remember that this section is more about HOW you discuss the issues raised both in terms of your own contribution and in supporting and respecting your team rather than WHAT you say.

Section 5

Task Prioritisation Written Exercise

The task prioritisation exercise

The third exercise that you will be assessed upon in your selection centre is the prioritisation exercise. It is a written paper.

This exercise is very different from the other two tasks. It is individually tested and is purely based on what you write down. There is no personal interaction and it is marked in your absence after you have completed the task.

The key to success with this exercise is to practise on as many examples as you can within the allocated time limit set by the selection centre. With an unlimited amount of time this task would be much easier. Having only 20 minutes (deanery dependent) to complete this exercise adds a huge amount of time pressure, which makes the task much more difficult.

The prioritisation exercise is definitely testing your ability to solve problems and work under pressure of time, your professional probity, thought processes and personal organisation. As you will see later it is also possibly testing your multidisciplinary teamworking skills and the effect upon you. The most important piece of advice I can give you is to remember to talk about the *effect upon you*. This is a key aspect of the prioritisation exercise and is often forgotten.

Well-run courses specifically aimed at the GPST interview process will go through examples of the prioritisation exercise in detail. They will also ideally allow you to practise in an examination style environment with the pressure of time added. If you cannot attend a course, at least practise the examples that follow in the book. Be tough on yourself. Perhaps try the first one with no time limit, but please make sure that you save at least one to do while the clock is ticking. It adds a completely different perspective to the task.

What will happen?

Read the information sent to you from your selection centre. Most centres will have 20 minutes in which to complete the prioritisation task. This may be split into two sections which will be explained later. Some centres may only have 10 minutes if based on the OSCE set-up. The principles are the same.

You will be taken as a group to an examination-type room and sat at individual desks with an invigilator present. This person is not assessing you during the exercise. Experienced examiners will score your paper after completion of the task once you have handed in your paper and left the room.

All candidates in your group will start the exercise at the same time.

The exercise

The general task is the same in all centres though there may be slight variations, which will be discussed later.

You will be given a group of simultaneous tasks that you need to rank in order of importance to perform. These tasks are usually based in primary or secondary care and you must answer them from your own perspective. The paper will tell you either:

a. *You are a doctor in secondary care*
    In this case you are likely to be an A&E or ward doctor (SHO/FY2 level) and have a number of sequential bleeps with tasks to complete. These tasks will be listed.

b. *You are a doctor based in primary care*
    In this case you are likely to be an SHO/FY2 doctor based in General Practise and have a list of tasks to complete. This is either in the form of messages left for you or sequential telephone calls. These tasks will be listed.

Not only are you asked to rank the tasks in the order that you would perform them but you also need to justify the order by explaining HOW you would complete each task and WHY you would put each task in the order that you did.

The number of tasks that you need to prioritise

The number of sequential bleeps or messages will differ depending on the allocation of time that your deanery gives to this task.

a. Twenty minutes: this is the standard time given by most deaneries. The number of tasks to prioritise is usually five or six. There is only one exercise to complete.

b. Ten minutes (OSCE-type assessment):
   i. There may only be three tasks to prioritise using the standard format, instead of the six that you would have to complete if you had double the time.
   ii. An alternative to this is based more on the situational judgement test that you completed at Stage 2 of the assessment process. In this case you will have approximately five exercises to complete, but you only have to rank the order of importance. There is no justification required. This is discussed more in practice prioritisation exercise 4.

The rest of this section will be dedicated to the standard format of prioritisation exercise as described in sections a and b(i) above. There are examples of all types of question later in the book.

The test paper (standard format)

There are two main ways to set out the question and answer paper and this will be deanery dependent.

Type 1 (the easier paper)

The paper will have an introductory statement about who you are and where you are based. It will then list each of the tasks in the order that they were received, in the form of a series of stems followed by a blank box below each stem where you can write your justification. This box limits your space for explanation to only four or five lines of writing.

For each stem, there will be a small box for you to place the ranking order into.

Figure 9. Type 1 prioritisation paper

Stem explaining that you are a doctor in primary or secondary care who has received a group of sequential messages or bleeps.

Message 1

Ranking number [ ]

Message 2

Ranking number [ ]

Message 3

Ranking number [ ]

Message 4

Ranking number [ ]

(In practice, there will likely be five or six messages to order and justify.)

There are two ways to approach this type of paper:

    a. Go through and justify each stem and then, at the end, ensure that you have saved some time (which is often in limited supply) to rank the tasks in the order that you would do them.

    b. First spend a few minutes deciding on the order that you would complete each task and rank them. Follow this by placing the justification in the boxes provided.

There is no right or wrong way to approach this paper. It very much depends on the manner with which you analyse situations. By practicing these exercises with a time limit, you will begin to work out which approach works better for you.

Like all of the tasks already described in this book, you need to work out your own approach. Do not regurgitate what is written here. Instead, use this book as a platform to provide you with ideas to try out to enable you to create your own style and approach.

Type 2 (the harder paper)

The principles are exactly the same as with the type 1 paper but you have to write the justifications in the order that you would perform the tasks.

The paper will have an introductory statement about who you are and where you are based and will list each of the tasks in the order that they were received. These will be numbered. You will then have a separate sheet with empty boxes. In the first box you will be expected to justify the first task that you would perform, in the second box the second, until the final task that you would leave to the very end.

The reason that this is more difficult is that you need to decide on the order of the tasks before you start to write. This often means making some very rapid decisions in the first few minutes of the assessment. Some of you will be very confident in doing this. For others who like to think and deliberate, it will take longer to make the decision. You may also feel less confident with the decisions made.

Figure 10. Type 2 prioritisation paper

Stem explaining that you are a doctor in primary or secondary care who has received a group of sequential messages or bleeps.

Message 1
Message 2
Message 3
Message 4
etc.

Justify the tasks in the boxes below in the order that you would complete them. A is the first task that you would complete.

A

B

C

D

(There will likely be five or six messages to justify and rank)

There are two ways to approach this type of paper:

a. First spend a few minutes deciding on the order that you would complete each task and then fill in the answer sheet in order from the first and most important task to the last and least important task.

b. Choose the task that you would obviously do first and fill in the first box. Choose the task that you would obviously do last and fill in the last box. Following this spend a few minutes thinking about the order of the rest and fill the boxes in as you see appropriate.

There is no right or wrong way to approach this paper. It will depend on your personality and confidence levels and the way that you analyse situations. By practicing these exercises with a time limit, you will begin to work out which approach works better for you.

Like all of the tasks already described in this book, you need to work out your own approach. Do not regurgitate what is written here. Instead, use this book as a platform to provide you with ideas to try out to enable you to create your own style and approach.

Ranking

Make sure that you follow the instructions given to you on the day. If the paper asks you to rank using the letters A-F, use these letters and nothing else. If the paper asks you to number the ranking from 1 to 6, use these numbers.

This may seem obvious, but with the added pressure of time it is easy to forget to read the instruction carefully. As this exercise is testing how you cope under pressure, a simple mistake like this may lose you valuable points. Don't risk it!

The blank boxes

The defined blank boxes are there for a reason. If the instructions state that you should only write within the defined space, please adhere to that. The examiners are unlikely to read anything outside of the box if this instruction is given. Don't waste time writing information that will not be assessed. Time is precious.

Mistakes

This task is assessing your thought processes and the way you approach a time-pressured task. Try to make your decision about the order that you would complete the tasks *before* committing this decision to the paper.

By having a clear thought process you are likely to score more points. The paper with five different rankings that have been scribbled out and changed is unlikely to score highly.

If you are the type of person who is likely to change their mind make notes elsewhere before committing to your decision. Use pencil that you can rub out. Some deaneries may not allow scrap paper, as they want to see your thought processes written down.

Additional tasks – reflective learning

Some deaneries will have an additional task to complete within the allocated time given. This is usually some form of reflective learning.

Those of you who have trained in the new system will have often had experience of reflective learning through medical school and throughout your foundation years of training. It is important in all aspects of medicine, and General Practice has embraced it wholeheartedly. Those of you in the old "traditional" system of training may have no experience at all and know little about it.

Reflective learning is not a complex concept. It can in fact be applied to any exercise or task completed and is often done subconsciously by many people.

A common situation in medical practice where reflective learning is practised is following an arrest call. Imagine that you were part of an arrest team where the patient sadly died. Rather than returning to A&E to see the next patient on our list, we often spend a little time thinking about what happened, what went well, what could have been done differently, what we found difficult and how we felt about the arrest call. This is reflective thinking. If we use some of that thinking to alter and improve our practice next time, then we have learnt from our experience. This is reflective learning.

This reflective approach is formalised in many medical schools' curriculums and in the foundation years of medical training. To most new graduates this

will be second nature. If you have trained in the old system or are from overseas, you may have no experience of this type of practice.

It often seems odd when you first start practicing it but, like everything else we have discussed in this book, with practice it becomes easier and more natural.

Practise the reflective learning with each of the examples in the book. In addition, start practicing every day to help this become a natural way of thinking. Set yourself a target to allocate 5 minutes each day to reflective learning. This can be done at work after seeing a patient; it could also be applied at home. An example of using it at home could be after making dinner. How well did it go? What did you do well? What did you find difficult? What would you do differently next time?

You can practise reflective learning at any time with any task. Remember, preparation and practice is the only way to improve.

Time

Time really is in short supply for this exercise. This factor alone increases the pressure attached to it. Try to plan your time as you practise the exercises in the book. You need to split the allocated time to ensure you complete the whole exercise.

In order to give effective answers, you must follow a thought process with which you are comfortable. Ultimately, you will each need to cover all of the following points, but it is up to you to decide what order to do them in.

1 – Read the brief

Who are you? Where are you? What criteria are given?
Is it a type 1 or type 2 paper?
Are you to use numbers or letters in your ranking?

Read it, read it and read it again to make sure that you have understood the task.

2 – Think about the ranking

Is there an obvious task to do first and last? Obvious options would include anything that would prevent a risk to a patient.

Is there a clear order for all of them?
Are there one or two options that could be placed in any order? How are you going to decide where to rank them?

3 – Decide on the ranking

You need to make a firm decision at some point in the exercise as to your final ranking order. Make this decision before confirming this on paper. Try not to make changes if you can.

4 – Justify your answers

Each of the tasks needs to be justified. Explain how you would perform the task and why you would place it where you have.

5 – Reflective learning (if requested by the brief)

This part of the exercise is as important as the first part. There are points awarded for this section. Candidates in the past did not leave enough time to complete this section thoroughly as they thought that it was more important to finalise the justifications. Do not fall into this trap.

6 – Check your answers

Ideally, as with any written task, a little time to check over your paper is always valuable. You may find that some of the rankings need tweaking or that you could justify one option more appropriately.

Effect on you

Some prioritisation tasks contain options that are of a more personal nature (i.e. they do not solely relate to patients). When facing such options, it is essential that you take into account how the situation is affecting you and your abilities to function both as a doctor and a human being.

At least one of the messages, tasks or bleeps that will be listed for you to rank will have a personal slant. This may be a personal phone call, a family crisis, an appointment that you need to keep or the fact that you are going on holiday. It is very important that you recognise their personal slant and that, in the justification, you write down how this would affect *you*.

There are several ways to approach this. I have met both extremes of doctors who would react very differently when faced with a personal message. As long as you justify clearly in your answer how it would affect you (if at all) then you can in theory place this in any order in the ranking.

Example

Scenario: *You are an SHO in A&E and one of your six bleeps is a message left with the senior ward nurse who asks you to contact your sister urgently.*

Possible answers:

a. You could rank this as the number one priority for you to complete (depending on the rest of the messages) if you justified it adequately.

My sister looks after my 1-year-old son whilst I am at work and the only time that she would ever call is if he were seriously ill.

You must recognise the effect on you:

I would be unable to concentrate on any task in front of me, suspecting that my son was ill, and so I would have to call her immediately to find out what had happened. I would therefore place this task first in the ranking.

I would be unable to concentrate on any task in front of me suspecting that my son was ill. I would need more information as soon as was possible. I would ask the ward nurse to call my sister back and get a full message regarding what was wrong whilst I attended the arrest call. I would ask the nurse to call another SHO to come and take over from me at the arrest call if it was a life or death situation in order for me to attend to my son.

Both of these justifications would allow you to rank your sister's call first.

b. You could rank this last, as long as you justified it adequately. *My sister calls me at work every day at least once. She calls me at home about six times a day. Her urgent calls are always relating to a fashion question. Can she borrow my jumper? Can she wear red trousers with orange shoes? Knowing that this is what her question is likely to be, I would place it much lower down in the list of priorities. My patients always come first.*

Depending on the other tasks, this type of justification would allow you to rank this "personal message" much lower down, perhaps even last.

The right answer

There is perhaps no absolute right and wrong way to order the messages or tasks; and much of the marking will be related to your justification. If you are aware of the GMC *Good Medical Practice,* this task will be much easier. The GMC's *Duties of a Doctor* clearly states that your patient always comes first. You must remember this but, as mentioned above, do not forget the effect on you, as a person and as a doctor.

Approaches to ranking

One approach is to look at the messages/ tasks that need to be completed and split them into categories. Some tasks may have a direct relationship with patient safety (e.g. a patient with chest pain at your surgery); others are also patient-related but maybe not so urgent (e.g. a complaint). You then have a range of tasks which have no immediate effect on patients (e.g. a colleague who wants to talk to you about an audit project). And finally, you have tasks which are of a personal nature (e.g. a phone call from your sister).

The tasks that will be presented to you will fit into one of these categories. There could be between one and three of each type in your list at the exam.

Figure 11. Suggested approach to ranking order in the prioritisation exercise

Patient	Clinical cases involving the patient directly:
	  ▪ Chest pain
	  ▪ Arrest call
	  ▪ Nurse request to see a patient on the ward.

Extended patient	Clinically associated cases involving non-urgent patient matters:
	  ▪ Relatives
	  ▪ Complaints
	  ▪ Death.

Other	No direct patient effect:
	  ▪ Completing the rota
	  ▪ A telephone call
	  ▪ Running late for a meeting or appointment.

In general, the prioritisation order should reflect the above categories, but remember that the tasks that have a personal slant to them may be ranked anywhere in the above scale depending on the effect that they may have on you. If a message or task could affect you or your work, justify it and place it higher up in the list of prioritisation.

Delegation

One of the most important questions to ask yourself before you start to write is: "Who have I got available to help?" This task is not about you being a superhero doctor and coping with everything alone. In real practice, we have other people in the team to help. Think about who you can ask to help. This involves all members of the multidisciplinary team both clinical and non-clinical staff. Think about the whole team.

When delegating, it is essential that you ensure that the team member you entrusted with the task actually completed it. You can add a sentence to cover this in your answer.

Figure 12. Team support

▪ Junior doctor	▪ Social worker
▪ Senior doctor	▪ Health visitor
▪ Nurse	▪ Midwife
▪ Specialist nurse	▪ Patient and patient representatives
▪ Nurse Consultant	▪ Bereavement officer
▪ District/community nurse	▪ PALS
▪ Occupational therapist	▪ Support staff
▪ Physiotherapist	▪ Clerical staff
▪ Speech therapist	▪ Cleaners
▪ Pharmacist	

This is not an exhaustive list and you may be able to think of others.

Need for further information

In some cases, the options may be difficult to rank because the information is not sufficient to determine whether the matter is important or not. For example, if one of the options states: "A security guard contacts you and asks you to move your car as it is badly parked", then your ranking will be different

depending on whether the car is stopping ambulances from accessing A&E, or whether it is just slightly sticking out in the normal car park.

If the car was blocking ambulance access and you were busy with an emergency, the best that you could do would be to give your keys to a colleague so that he could move the car for you, or to ask the colleague to take over from you so that you can go and move your own car. It would feature high on your list of tasks and you would be able to sort things out through suitable delegation.

If the car was just annoying a few visitors, then it would be the least of your priorities in relation to other more pressing matters; you would then prioritise it last.

The main problem is that you just don't know what the situation is. What matters though is that there is a risk that it may be in a dangerous place (patient safety is potentially affected). In this situation, you would therefore need to gain more information from the security guard, which would take 5 seconds (in fact a secretary could do it for you if you were busy) and you can then advise.

This is a case of a situation where a seemingly non-patient-related matter could potentially impact on patient care. Overall, it would therefore rank high, simply because of the potential risk to patients, and you would need to explain the dilemma that you face together with the need to use colleagues to sort the situation out.

Additional comments

It is unlikely that any comments written outside the boxes will be given any marks, but if you have time – and ONLY if you have time – there are a few additional comments that may be appropriate to write as a brief introduction and brief conclusion. Some of these comments could actually also be included in the main body of your justifications.

Comments that may be relevant include:
a. Recognising that the task is difficult.

b. Recognising that time is very limited.

c. Recognising the need for further information.

d. Recognising the need to utilise all members of the multidisciplinary team available to you including both clinical and non-clinical staff.

e. Recognising the need to delegate where possible. This includes delegating down to junior colleagues, across to your peers, up to senior colleagues and to other members of the multidisciplinary team where appropriate.

f. Stating what you would normally do in situations like that described. Examples would include writing a "to do" list or calling a colleague to help.

g. Reviewing the workload and reprioritising where possible (i.e. once you have prioritised, circumstances might change and you need to remain adaptable to varying circumstances).

h. Recognising the effect on you and the need for time out and debriefing, particularly after a stressful situation.

Assessment criteria

The prioritisation exercise is definitely testing your ability to solve problems, work under pressure of time, your professional probity, thought processes and personal organisation, your multidisciplinary teamworking skills and the effect upon you.

The marking schedule will therefore take account of a range of factors, including many from the list below:

1 – Written skills

If the assessor cannot read your writing, they will be unable to give you your mark. You will need to write quickly during this exercise.

Try to make your handwriting as legible as you can.

Practise at least one of the exercises that follow with the time limit applied.

Look at your writing. Can you read it?
Ask a colleague. Can they read it?

2 – Approach

Did you think about the tasks and messages before you started writing?
Did you make any logical notes?
Are there multiple scribbles on your paper because you changed your mind over and over again?

3 – Thought process

Is your thinking and justification clear?
Does it make sense?
Is it appropriate?
Do you have multiple mistakes crossed out because you changed your mind?

4 – Emergency case

Did you recognise that there was a clinical case that needed urgent attention?
Did you put the patient first?
Are you a safe doctor?
It is essential to deal with the clinical emergency as a first priority.

5 – Ranking

Did you rank the tasks as requested?
Did you use the correct lettering/ numbering scheme?
Is the ranking appropriate? Do the "patient-centred" tasks come before the "extended patient" tasks? Do the "other" tasks rank lower down?

6 – Teamwork

Did you use the team?
Did you think about clinical and non-clinical members of the multidisciplinary team?
Was the delegation appropriate?
Should you have completed more tasks yourself?
Did you state anywhere that you would check to see if the tasks had been completed and get follow-up from your team members?

7 – Time management

Did you complete the exercise?
Did you leave time for the reflective learning (if present)?
Are your answers to the first two stems very long with only a sentence for the other stems?
Did you rush the last few stems?

8 – Effect on you

Did you acknowledge the effect that one or more of the tasks had on you, the person?
Did you explain this in your answer?
Was your ranking appropriate when taking into account the effect on you?

9 – Reflective learning (if present)

Did you leave enough time for the reflective learning?
Did you complete all sections requested?
Did you learn anything from the exercise?
Were you open to the fact that we all make mistakes?
Did you acknowledge your limitations?
Did you appreciate what you did well?
Is there anything that you would do differently next time after experiencing this exercise?
Did you learn anything about yourself?

How to prepare for the day

Practise, practise, practise. Start by thinking about what you do in your everyday life, when you are at work and on call. How do you organise and prioritise your time and tasks? When you are at home, how do you juggle your home commitments such as childcare, cooking, shopping and cleaning with your social life and work life? What techniques do you employ?

Make sure that the way that you handle the written task reflects your own skills. Write down how *you* would prioritise, not how you think it should be prioritised or how this book (or others) tells you to prioritise.

Once you have thought about your own techniques, use the exercises in the book to practise. Make sure you do at least one example with a stopwatch

and the added pressure of time. Write down the answers in full as you would do on the day and ask someone else to read them.

You will of course pick up some things by just reading through the exercises, but you will gain so much more by working through them in an examination environment.

The gold standard once again is to find a reputable and well-respected course that will allow you to practise with trained tutors. Make sure it has a focus on the written/ prioritisation exercise and has a small number of candidates. Listen to the feedback and learn from the other participants. See what works well and what doesn't. Use everything that you can to improve and prepare for the day.

Figure 13. Suggested assessment criteria for the written prioritisation exercise

1. Written skills
2. Approach
3. Thought process
4. Emergency case
5. Ranking
   - Patient
   - Extended Patient
   - Other
6. Teamwork
7. Time management
8. Effect on you
9. Reflective learning

Section 6

Task Prioritisation
Practice Exercises

How to use this section

As already mentioned, the best way to prepare is to practise and have a go. In this section, you will find examples of prioritisation exercises that you can use to practise.

If you simply read through the examples, you will pick up some information, but you will gain so much more by writing them out. To do this effectively, you need to allow yourself 20 minutes of uninterrupted time. Turn off your mobile phone, the radio and the television. Draw out a marking sheet with limited space for your answers or write in the spaces provided in the book, and only look at the question under a time pressured "examination" setting. Try to keep at least one of the following examples to practise in this way

Ask a colleague to look at your written answer after you have completed the exercise. Get them to mark you based on the criteria discussed above.

The preparation exercises

Each of the following exercises will try to recreate a type of question that you may get on the day. There are both type 1 "easier" and type 2 "more difficult" examples, as discussed above. Each question can be answered in either way. Practise both types.

There is one practice question that relates more to the OSCE 10-minute assessment. In this question there are five stems. For each stem you need to rank the order in which you would perform the tasks. There is no justification required. This type of question is more like the situational judgement paper that you sat at Stage 2 of the assessment process. The way it is marked is different and will be discussed separately with the practice question.

Please read the brief given to you by your individual deanery. This will tell you the timing and structure of each of the three assessed exercises.

Discussion

Following each of the practice questions, there will be a discussion based upon the suggested assessment criteria. I have also provided one possible answer. Remember that there is often no absolute right and wrong answer.

Task Prioritisation Practice Exercise 1

Simple

Task Prioritisation Exercise 1

Examination Paper

You are an SHO/ FY2 doctor based in A&E and have 1 hour left until the end of your 12-hour shift. There are normally two doctors covering each shift.

You have just returned to the department after escorting a patient to the intensive care unit when the senior nurse approaches you. She explains that the second doctor who should be covering the department has a severe migraine and has had to go and lie down. The senior nurse tells you that the department is very busy and she will try to find someone to help. She has written down a list of things that you need to do urgently.

You need to explain how you would proceed with each task, why you would respond in that particular way and then finally rank the order in which you would perform the tasks from A to F.

A is the first task that you would perform and F is the task that you would leave until last.

Messages

1. The Consultant from intensive care has called. He wants to speak to you about the patient that you have transferred to them. There are some notes missing from the patient file.

Ranking ☐

2. As you are reading the list of messages you hear a nurse shouting for assistance in the resuscitation room. They are asking for the resuscitation trolley and defibrillator.

Ranking ☐

>>>> Continues next page >>>>

3. A message has been left to call the nursery that your son attends.

Ranking ☐

4. There is a patient waiting to see you in the "majors" area of A&E who is having a heavy PV bleed. The nurse has noted down the possibility of a miscarriage. Pregnancy test is positive.

Ranking ☐

>>>> Continues next page >>>>

5. The blood bank technician has called. A "group and save" blood request that you sent through to them earlier is not labelled properly. They need you to go to the laboratory and confirm the patient details.

Ranking [ ]

6. An SHO/ FY2 doctor has called you and left a message for you to ring back about the mess party later that night.

Ranking [ ]

>>>> Continues next page >>>>

Reflective learning

1. What single thing did you find difficult about the exercise?

2. What two things did you find easy about the exercise?

3. What have you learnt from completing this exercise about yourself?

4. What one thing would you do differently next time?

Task Prioritisation Exercise 1

Discussion

Read the brief

Did you spend time reading the brief?
Who are you?
Where are you based?
What job are you doing?
How much time do you have left on your shift?
Who is available to help you?

You know that you are working in A&E and therefore have a whole team of people to help out. This will include doctors from other specialities, nurses, and clerical staff amongst many others.

Who could you use to help with each task?

Task 1

Perhaps the receptionist or A&E "ward clerk" could help with the missing notes. They could contact ITU and find out exactly what is missing. It may be a simple case of the X-rays not being transferred with the patient. It could also be that the notes that are missing are the handwritten notes that you wrote after seeing the patient.

By writing in your justification:

I always complete my handwritten notes before moving on to the next patient; so any notes that are missing must be in the A&E department somewhere.

you would easily be able to justify delegating the finding and transportation of these notes to ITU to a member of the team. This would leave you free to complete the clinical tasks.

Task 2

If a nurse is shouting for help in an arrest situation and you are the only doctor in the department, you must complete this task yourself. Once you get to the arrest, things may change. When the medical or anaesthetic staff arrive, you could ask to leave the arrest team if appropriate.

Task 3

You could delegate this to a member of the non-clinical team to contact the nursery on your behalf to get more information about your son whilst you dealt with the emergency clinical cases. By asking the nominated member of your team to find you as soon as they have more information, you will ensure that you receive the information as quickly as you possibly can. Once you know what the problem is you can then deal with it appropriately.

Task 4

There is already a nurse present with this patient; however, they are asking for your help with a PV bleed. It is important to support your team and so would be essential for a doctor to attend. You can either do this yourself, or ask the nurse to contact the on-call gynaecology team explaining about the case and the fact that there is only one doctor in the department and asking for their help until you are free to attend.

Task 5

The failure to label a blood bank form adequately is your responsibility. You will need to go to the lab yourself to complete the details. If you are unable to attend the blood bank and the patient needs a crossmatch for blood transfusion soon, there are two options.

- a. You could ask the nurses/ phlebotomist to rebleed the patient.
- b. An alternative would be to ask a member of your team to go to the blood bank to retrieve the sample and bring it to you in the A&E department.

Task 6
This sounds like a personal call and you should therefore return the call yourself.

More information required

In all cases where messages of this type are left, we would always need to ascertain more information. This should be added to your justification.

Task 1

Before dealing with the missing notes I would ask the ward clerk to call ITU and find out exactly what notes were missing to enable me to deal with this task swiftly and efficiently.

Task 2

I would attend the arrest call immediately. This is an emergency and would need my urgent attention. Once present, depending on the clinical case and other team members present, I may or may not need to stay for the duration of the arrest.

Task 3

I need to know exactly what the problem with my son is before making a decision on how to proceed. I would ask the ward clerk/ nurse to call the nursery while I attended the arrest to ask what the problem was.

Task 4

To assess the clinical urgency of this case I would need more information. The nurse is asking for my help and so I would ensure that I attended as soon as I could. To decide how soon to attend, I would ask the attending nurse for more information. How many weeks pregnant is the woman? If she was 20 weeks pregnant or more, our local hospital policy is to transfer the woman to the antenatal ward. How heavily is she bleeding? What are her vital signs? (BP, HR, respiratory rate). Does she have a venflon and intravenous infusion? How much pain is she in?

Task 5

I would want to know the urgency of this "group and save" sample. I would hope that I would remember the patient and be able to make a rapid decision

as to whether this task could wait until I had completed the more urgent clinical cases.

Task 6
The mess party call could wait until I had completed all other tasks.

The assessment criteria

Remember the assessment criteria? (See Figure 13 p.195.)

1 – Written skills

If the assessor cannot read your writing, they will be unable to give you the marks that you deserve.

Look at your writing. Can you read it?
Is it clear? Do you understand what you have written down?
Ask a colleague. Can they read it?

2 – Approach

Did you think about the tasks and messages before you started writing?
Did you make any logical notes?
Are there multiple scribbles on your paper because you changed your mind over and over again?
What could you do differently next time?

If you didn't make notes, try making them during the next practice exercise. You may find that it helps.
If you did make notes, did they help? Did they confuse you? Did you waste precious time writing them?

3 – Thought process

Is your thinking and justification clear?
Does it make sense? Is it appropriate?
Cross-check your justification with the ranking that you gave them.

Did you cross out multiple mistakes because you changed your mind?
What would you do differently next time?

Is there something you could do to help clarify your thoughts?

Did you try splitting the messages into "patient", "extended patient" and "other"?

"Patient"

> 2. As you are reading the list of messages you hear a nurse shouting for assistance in the resuscitation room. They are asking for the resuscitation trolley and defibrillator.

> 4. There is a patient waiting to see you in the "majors" area of A&E who is having a heavy PV bleed. The nurse has noted down the possibility of a miscarriage. Pregnancy test is positive.

"Extended patient"

> 1. The Consultant from intensive care has called. He wants to speak to you about the patient that you have transferred to them. There are some notes missing from the patient file.

> 5. The blood bank technician has called. A "group and save" blood request that you sent through to them earlier is not labelled properly. They need you to go to the laboratory and confirm the patient details.

"Other"

> 3. A message has been left to call the nursery that your son attends.

> 6. An SHO/ F2 doctor has called you and left a message for you to ring back about the mess party later that night.

By splitting the six messages into these categories it often helps to clarify the general order that the messages should be ranked into.

4 – The emergency case

Did you recognise that there was a clinical case that needed urgent attention?

In this list of messages the shout for help from the nurse with the arrest call would be your first and most urgent priority.

Did you put the patient first as suggested in the GMC guidance?
Are you a safe doctor?

5 – Ranking

Did you rank the tasks as requested?
Did you use the correct lettering scheme?

The brief stated that you should use A-F with A being the first priority and F being the least priority case. Did you follow this?

Is your ranking appropriate?
Do the "patient-centred" tasks come before the "extended patient" tasks?
Do the "other" tasks rank lower down?

The one exception to this may be the telephone call about your son and the effect on you. This "other" task may have ranked higher than an "extended patient" or even a "patient" task depending on your justification.

Suggested ranking
Assuming that a call from your son's nursery did not affect you at all – which is highly unlikely – the ranking you decided upon is likely to be one of the following:

1	2	
A 2	A 2	Message 2 must come first as it is an arrest situation.
B 4	B 4	Message 4 is an urgent clinical case and should come second.
C 5	C 1	Message 1 from the ITU about the missing notes is
D 1	D 5	important to deal with as it will indirectly affect a patient's care. Message 5 from the blood bank is also important to deal with, as this again will directly or indirectly affect patient care. The order in which you choose to rank messages 1 and 5 will depend on how you choose to justify your choice.

E 3	E 3	Making the unlikely assumption that message 3 (the
F 6	F 6	phone call about your son) would not affect you at all
		would place this lower down in the ranking. This is still
		more important than a social call about a mess party
		and so message 6 would definitely rank lowest at F.

Remember that there is no absolute answer. If you allocated a greater weight to the phone call about your son then your ranking and justifications would be different. See paragraph 8.

6 – Teamwork

Did you use the team?

Did you think about clinical and non-clinical members of the multidisciplinary team?

Was the delegation appropriate?
Should you have completed more tasks yourself?
Should you have completed fewer tasks yourself?

Did you state anywhere that you would check to see if the tasks had been completed and get follow-up from your team members?

7 – Time management

Did you complete the exercise?
Did you leave time for the reflective learning?

Are your answers to the first two stems very long with only a sentence for the other stems? Did you rush the last few stems?

Did you have time to make a clear decision on the ranking or did you feel rushed into it?
How would you allocate the time better if you had to run the exercise again? Is there a better way?

8 – Effect on you

Did you acknowledge that the telephone call about your son in message 3 would have an effect on you, the person?

Did you explain this in your answer?

> *The nursery never calls me about my son at work unless something is seriously wrong. I would not be able to concentrate until I knew he was OK.*

Justifying your answer in this way would allow you to place this "other" task much higher on your list of priorities. I do not think that you could justify putting it above the arrest call as this is a major emergency, but you could easily justify putting it second or third in the list.

The only way in which you could justify prioritising the call about your son as the first task on your list is if you delegated the phone call to someone else. For example, by stating that you would quickly ask the ward clerk (who was sitting at the desk in front of you) to contact the nursery and come to find you at the arrest call if your son was in any danger, you would be able to handle both your son and the arrest call as top priorities.

Was your ranking appropriate when taking into account the effect on you?

Other possible ranking, recognising that message 3 would have an effect on you and how you would work, includes the following:

If you wanted to deal with your son first		If you dealt with the arrest call first and then your son		If you dealt with all the "patient" tasks first and then your son	
A 3	A 3	A 2	A 2	A 2	A 2
B 2	B 2	B 3	B 3	B 4	B 4
C 4	C 4	C 4	C 4	C 3	C 3
D 5	D 1	D 5	D 1	D 5	D 1
E 1	E 5	E 1	E 5	E 1	E 5
F 6	F 6	F 6	F 6	F 6	F 6

As you can see, your justification influences your ranking significantly. However, there is a general order of ranking that must be adhered to.

9 – Reflective learning

Did you leave enough time for the reflective learning?
Did you complete all sections requested?
Did you give the correct number of examples for each section?
Did you learn anything from the exercise?
Were you open to the fact that we all make mistakes?
Did you acknowledge your limitations?
Did you appreciate what you did well?

Is there anything that you would do differently next time after experiencing this exercise?

Did you learn anything about yourself?

There is potentially a great deal of information that you could write in each of the boxes provided. You need to decide what information is important in each case, justify how and why you would do each task and rank them according to your explanation. Remember: practise, practise, practise.

Prioritisation Exercise 1

Sample answer

To help you to understand how to approach the written prioritisation question, read the following suggested appropriate answer. This is not a perfect answer and should not be regurgitated in an assessment situation. Remember that everyone will approach the question in a slightly different way and that there is no absolute answer. What is important is how you approach it, managing your time and ensuring that you are practising safe medicine. What follows is one option of ranking for the task.

1. The consultant from intensive care has called. He wants to speak to you about the patient that you have transferred to them. There are some notes missing from the patient file.

This task, if not resolved, may have a significant impact on a very sick (ITU) patient. I know how important documentation is and how crucial a handover is in patient management. I personally always complete my handwritten notes before moving on to the next patient so any missing notes must be in the A&E department somewhere. I would ask the ward clerk or nurse in charge to contact ITU to find out more information, asking exactly what notes were missing and ensuring that they passed on my apologies to the consultant for not calling back myself. I would always ensure that the person I designated to the task reported back to me to make sure that the notes had been found and therefore the ITU patient was safe and the staff were happy. I would finally contact the ITU consultant later in the day to reiterate my apologies for not returning his call. It is always worth reporting this type of mistake to the nurse in charge to allow them to investigate what went wrong and to try and prevent it happening again in the future

Ranking = D

2. As you are reading the list of messages you hear a nurse shouting for assistance in the resuscitation room. They are asking for the resuscitation trolley and defibrillator.

This is an emergency and would need my urgent attention. Ensuring my own safety and the safety of the patient I was with (if I was currently with one), I would drop everything and attend the arrest call. The patient should always come first and the arresting patient is a life-threatening situation. For this reason I would rank this first. I know that I am the only doctor in the department and must attend. Once the full arrest team arrive with anaesthetist and medical team, I may be able to hand the case over and carry on with my other tasks. I would not leave until it was safe to do so, or until I was certain that the arrest was being handled appropriately.

Ranking = A

3. A message has been left to call the nursery that your son attends.

If my son were at nursery, I am certain that the only time that the nursery would call me at work would be in a serious situation. It may be that my son has been taken ill and I would therefore need to call back as soon as I could. I know that I would not be able to fully concentrate on work until I knew what was wrong. The call would be very quick and so I would either ask the ward clerk (who I have a very good relationship with) to call them and ask exactly what the nature of the problem was and its urgency whilst I dealt with the arrest call or I would call the nursery myself the minute I was free from the life-threatening patient arrest situation. Once I knew the extent of the problem I may need to reprioritise my tasks or hand over my tasks to ensure my son was ok.

Ranking = B

4. There is a patient waiting to see you in the "majors" area of A&E who is having a heavy PV bleed. The nurse has noted down the possibility of a miscarriage. Pregnancy test is positive.

This task is not as urgent as an arrest call. There is already a trained nurse with the patient so the patient is in relative safety, but I know how important it is to support my team so I would want to attend as soon as I possibly could. I would try to get some more information from the nurse including the patient's vital signs (HR, BP, RR and oxygen saturations) in addition to the degree of pain and bleeding she was experiencing. If the patient was in a critical condition or it was a possible ruptured ectopic pregnancy and I couldn't attend, I would ask the nurse to contact the on-call gynaecology team, apologise and explain the extraordinary situation in A&E asking for them to attend and help. If the patient was stable I would attend as soon as I was free. Whilst waiting for me I would ask if the nurse could do some baseline investigations including bloods and to site a venflon for IV access with the addition of commencing intravenous fluids if appropriate.

Ranking = C

5. The blood bank technician has called. A "group and save" blood request that you sent through to them earlier is not labelled properly. They need you to go to the laboratory and confirm the patient details.

This task could have an impact on patient care so I would want to deal with this as soon as I could. I have clearly made a mistake and know how important it is to label all forms correctly but this is even more relevant with blood bank crossmatch/ group and save forms. I would first want more information (if I could not remember the case); what test, how urgent was it and what were the correct patient details. All this information I could get from a staff nurse or ward clerk and blood bank staff. If the blood was required urgently for a patient who was bleeding and I couldn't attend, I could ask a nurse or phlebotomist to rebleed the patient, sending my apologies to the patient for my mistake to ensure a rapid response. If the blood was not urgent, I would ensure that I attended the blood bank as soon as it was possible to correct my mistake. I would try to ensure that this never happened again by acknowledging what my mistake was and ensuring I was more precise in the future.

Ranking = E

6. An SHO/ F2 doctor has called you and left a message for you to ring back about the mess party later that night.

This is a non-clinical task and should be ranked last as it not essential to deal with straight away. Even if I were organising the mess party, this task could wait until I had finished all my clinical tasks.

Ranking = F

Task Prioritisation Practice Exercise 2

Advanced

Task Prioritisation Exercise 2

Examination paper

You are an FY2/SHO doctor based in primary care. You are at the end of your 4-month attachment and the partners allow you to see patients independently, asking for help whenever you need it.

It is 11:00. The only other doctor in the surgery is a partner. The partner calls you stating that there is an emergency home visit that he is going to attend leaving you in the surgery alone. He aims to be back before the end of surgery at 12:00 to help you finish. He leaves.

The following tasks need completing.

Task 1	The receptionist calls you. A man has approached the desk and is angry that he is having to wait. His appointment was at 10:50. The receptionist states that he is shouting and threatening to complain.
Task 2	You have an appointment at the hospital to see a Consultant about your own health at 12:15. Your last patient had been booked in at 11:00, which would have given you time to get there.
Task 3	The practice nurse calls you. There is a patient having an acute asthma attack in her room. She requests your help.
Task 4	There is a telephone call from a patient. A wasp has stung her 2-year-old daughter. Her face has started to swell up. She is struggling to breathe.
Task 5	The senior practice nurse needs a prescription signing for some antibiotics. The patient is with her and is in a rush to leave.
Task 6	A drug representative is waiting to see you.

Justify how you would complete the tasks in the boxes below in the order that you would complete them. A is the first task that you would complete. F is the last task that you would complete.

A

B

C

>>>> Continues next page >>>>

D

E

F

Reflective learning

1. What two things did you find difficult about the exercise?

2. What one thing did you find easy about the exercise?

3. What have you learnt from completing this exercise about yourself?

4. What two things would you do differently next time?

Prioritisation Exercise 2

Discussion

Read the brief

Did you spend time reading the brief?
Who are you?
Where are you based?
What job are you doing?
How much time do you have left on your shift?

Who is available to help you?

You know that you are working in General Practice. You know that you are the only doctor, but have with you the rest of the General Practice team. The brief mentions a senior nurse, a nurse and a receptionist. There are often other people present in General Practice.

Is there a medical student?
Does the practice have a pharmacist, counsellor or other allied staff?
Is there another doctor/ partner who you could call in?
We tend to carry mobile phones with us. Could you call the partner?
What about the practice manager?

Who could you use to help with each task?

Task 1

The angry patient is only running 10 minutes late for his appointment. You could ask the receptionist if they would explain to all the patients waiting about the emergency and apologise for any delay. You could ask them to put up a sign. You could ask them to offer another appointment to any patient who feels that they have a non-urgent case and could wait for another day.

Task 2

It is important that you look after your own health. The GMC's *Good Medical Practice* states that you must be registered with a GP and acknowledge and recognise any ill health in yourself. You must try to attend this appointment.

You could ask if there is another partner at home who could come in and cover; you could also telephone the partner on the home visit explaining that you need to leave and asking them to come back as soon as they can.

The best person to help in this situation is the practice manager. Contact them and explain the need for you to leave and the exceptional situation that you are in. Ask for his or her help to find someone to cover for you if the partner is not back in time.

Task 3

The patient having an acute asthma attack will need your input. The brief states in task 5 that there is a senior nurse in the practice. Could you ask her to help? Can the nurses set up and give nebulisers? Asking for the nurse's help will allow you to attend to the patient but you will not necessarily have to stay with them. This will allow you to attend to other tasks.

Task 4

This sounds like it could be an anaphylactic reaction and so you will need to deal with this quickly. The child may need intramuscular adrenaline. The parent should be told to call the paramedics immediately. It is often quicker (unless you are a rural GP) to send the paramedics rather than visit the patient or get the parents to bring the child to the surgery.

Task 5

The prescription will need signing and, if you know the patient, their allergies and sensitivities will be quick to complete. You can ask the nurse to help explain to the patient the problem in the surgery and, if the patient has to leave, you could suggest that they leave the prescription and return later to pick it up once it has been signed.

Task 6

You could ask the receptionist to explain to the drug rep that you have been held up, suggesting an alternative appointment.

More information required

In all cases where messages of this type are left we would always need to ascertain more information. This should be added to your justification.

Task 1

No further information is required. You may wish to know how many patients are waiting and how many are non-urgent and willing to rebook an appointment for another day.

Task 2

You may wish to call the hospital clinic and explain that you may be late. Is the clinic running on time? Would the Consultant still see you if you turned up late?

Task 3

You would need to know information about the patient. How old are they? Are they a known asthmatic? What are their respiratory rate, blood pressure, heart rate and peak flow? Can they talk in sentences? Can the nurse give nebulisers?

Task 4

How far away is the patient? If she lives next door to the practice then her mum could bring her straight in. Otherwise, the paramedics would be quicker to respond.

Task 5

No further information is required.

Task 6

No further information is required.

The assessment criteria

Remember the assessment criteria? (See Figure 13 p.195.)

1 – Written skills

If the assessor cannot read your writing, they will be unable to give you the marks that you deserve.

Look at your writing. Can you read it?
Is it clear? Do you understand what you have written down?
Ask a colleague. Can they read it?

2 – Approach

Did you think about the tasks and messages before you started writing?
Did you make any logical notes?
Are there multiple scribbles on your paper because you changed your mind over and over again?
What could you do differently next time?

If you didn't make notes, try making them during the next practice exercise. You may find that it helps. If you did make notes, did they help?

Did they confuse you? Did you waste precious time writing them?

3 – Thought process

Is your thinking and justification clear?
Does it make sense?
Is it appropriate?
Cross-check your justification with the ranking that you gave them.

Did you cross out multiple mistakes because you changed your mind?
What would you do differently next time?

Is there something you could do to help clarify your thoughts?

Did you try splitting the messages into "patient", "extended patient" and "other"?

"Patient"

Task 3: The practice nurse calls you. There is a patient having an acute asthma attack in her room. She requests your help.

Task 4: There is a telephone call from a patient. A wasp has stung her 2-year-old daughter. Her face has started to swell up. She is struggling to breathe.

"Extended patient"

Task 1: The receptionist calls you. There are many patients in the waiting room to be seen. One man has approached the desk and is angry that he is having to wait. His appointment was at 10:50. The receptionist states that he is shouting and threatening to complain.

Task 5: The senior practice nurse needs a prescription signing for some antibiotics. The patient is with her and is in a rush to leave.

"Other"

Task 2: You have an appointment at the hospital to see a Consultant about your own health at 12:15. Your last patient had been booked in at 11:00, which would have given you time to get there.

Task 6: A drug representative is waiting to see you.

By splitting the six messages into these categories it often helps to clarify the general order that the messages should be ranked into.

4 – The emergency case

Did you recognise that there were two clinical cases that needed urgent attention?
Both the acute asthma attack and the possible anaphylaxis need immediate attention. The telephone call about the anaphylaxis is likely to be very quick. Perhaps this should be ranked first?

Did you put the patient first as suggested in the GMC guidance?
Are you a safe doctor?

5 – Ranking

Did you rank the tasks as requested?

Did you place the first task in box A and the last task in box F?
How did you fill them in?

Did you decide on the obvious last and clear first task and then fill in the other boxes?
Did you fill in the boxes in order?

Whichever way you tried, did it work for you? Is it worth trying the exercise again approaching it in a different way?

Is your ranking appropriate?

Do the "patient-centred" tasks come before the "extended patient" tasks?
Do the "other" tasks rank lower down?

The one exception to this is task 2. You have an appointment about your own health, which you need to attend. Did you recognise the effect on you?

This "other" task should definitely have ranked higher than the drug rep and may have ranked higher than an "extended patient".

Suggested ranking:

A 4 B 3	Both 4 and 3 are "patient" tasks. It doesn't really matter which order you place these two cases in as long as they are in A and B. Both need your urgent clinical attention.
C 1 D 5	Both 1 and 5 are "extended patient" tasks. It doesn't matter which order you place them in. I would suggest that they should be in C and D. They will both be reasonably quick to resolve with help.
E 2 F 6	Both 2 and 6 are "other" tasks. The drug rep is definitely the least important, but we must recognise that we need to respect our colleagues and apologise to the drug rep.

Remember that there is no absolute answer. See below for an alternative answer when you recognise the effect of some of the tasks on you.

6 – Teamwork

Did you use the team?

Did you think about clinical and non-clinical members of the multidisciplinary team? Was the delegation appropriate?

Should you have completed more tasks yourself?

Should you have completed fewer tasks yourself?

Did you state anywhere that you would check to see if the tasks had been completed and get follow-up from your team members?

7 – Time management

Did you complete the exercise?
Did you leave time for the reflective learning?

Are your answers to the first two stems very long with only a sentence for the other stems?
Did you rush the last few stems?

Did you have time to make a clear decision on the ranking or did you feel rushed into it?

How would you allocate the time better if you had to run the exercise again? Is there a better way?

8 – Effect on you

Did you acknowledge that the need to leave on time to attend an appointment yourself would have an effect on you, the person?

Did you explain this in your answer?

> *I understand that my own health is important and the GMC points this out in their guide Good Medical Practice. I would ensure that I had support from colleagues and work as efficiently as I could to ensure that I reached my appointment on time. Informing the practice manager early in my list of tasks would make it more likely that I was able to leave when I needed to.*

Justifying your answer in this way would allow you to place this "other" task much higher on your list of priorities. I am not sure you could justify putting it above the urgent clinical cases (task 3 and 4), but you could easily justify putting it third, fourth or fifth on the list.

Was your ranking appropriate when taking into account the effect on you?

If you took account of the effect of task 2 on you or your work by making sure that you attend your appointment, having discussed the situation with the practice manager, you could derive the following ranking:

A 4
B 3
C 2
D 1
E 5
F 6

As you can see, your justification influences your ranking significantly. There is, however, a general order of ranking that must be adhered to.

9 – Reflective learning

Did you leave enough time for the reflective learning?
Did you complete all sections requested?
Did you give the correct number of examples for each section?

Did you learn anything from the exercise?
Were you open to the fact that we all make mistakes?
Did you acknowledge your limitations?
Did you appreciate what you did well?

Is there anything that you would do differently next time after experiencing this exercise?

Did you learn anything about yourself?

There is a great deal of information that you could write in each of the boxes provided. You need to decide what information is important in each case, justify how and why you would do each task, and rank them according to your explanation. Remember: practise, practise, practise.

Prioritisation Exercise 2

Sample Answer

To help you to understand how to approach the written prioritisation question, read the following suggested appropriate answer. This is not a perfect answer and should not be regurgitated in an assessment situation. Remember that everyone will approach the question in a slightly different way and that there is no absolute answer. What is important is how you approach it, managing your time and ensuring that you are practicing safe medicine. What follows is one option of ranking for the task.

A

Task 4. The telephone call regarding a 2 year old with a wasp sting and possible anaphylaxis is a "patient" task and potentially life-threatening. This should be dealt with as a top priority. The parents should be told to call 999 and wait for a rapid response paramedic who may give IM adrenaline and oxygen. If the patient lived next to the GP surgery I would also attend the patient whilst waiting for the paramedics, taking the resuscitation equipment and IM adrenaline with me. If the patient did not live close to the surgery, I could delegate the task of calling the parents to a receptionist or the practice nurse explaining that they must call 999, but in view of the highly anxious state that the parents are likely to be in I would rather deal with this myself (if I were able to) to support the parents through this difficult time whilst awaiting the ambulance.

B

Task 3. The patient with the asthma attack is a serious "patient" task and I would need to attend as soon as I could for the patient's benefit, but also to support my team (i.e. the nurse). The brief states that the nurse is a senior nurse and so I am certain that she could do basic observations and set up oxygen and a nebuliser to help stabilise the patient whilst I dealt with the more urgent task 4. I would want more information about the patient in terms of age, sex and observations. Can they talk in sentences? What are their saturations, HR, RR and BP? Have they ever had an attack before? Is there any wheeze or a silent chest? If the nurse could give a nebuliser I would ask her to set it up and to stay with the patient until I could get there.

C

Task 5 directly involves patient care that is less urgent. The nurse has decided on a treatment but needs it authorised. I would want more information regarding the illness, antibiotic sensitivities and patient allergies but this task would be quick to complete and I would ask the nurse to bring the prescription to me to save me time. If I were unable to sign it straight away and the patient had to leave, taking into account how serious the infection was that needed treating, I could ask the nurse to apologise to the patient and ask them to return to pick up the prescription at the end of the morning once things had calmed down. I could then spend more time checking the prescription before issuing it.

D

Task 1. The angry patient is not an acute clinical issue but will affect the team (particularly the receptionists) in addition to the other patients in the waiting room and so should be dealt with as soon as is possible. An ideal situation would be to ask the receptionists or the practice manager to explain to all the patients in the waiting room that there has been an emergency and that there will be an inevitable delay adding an apology to this. The receptionists could ask if any patient with a non-urgent illness would be prepared to rebook to see a doctor at another time, or to see the nurse if she had appointments free. I would want to know how many patients were waiting and would like to be able to explain to the man that he is only 10 minutes late for his appointment (it is now 1100) and he will be seen as soon as possible. It is also important to explain the complaints procedure and offer for him to see the practice manager to discuss his concerns.

E

Task 2. It is important that we look after our own health and indeed is one of the statements in the GMC guide *Good Medical Practice*. It is clearly important that I attend my outpatient appointment and therefore need to leave on time. I would firstly ask the practice manager if they could help by making them aware of my situation. It may be that we could postpone some patients or that he/she could call the partner ensuring his return to the practice on-time. I would hope that the practice was already aware of my need to leave as I always ensure good communication with my team to ensure (as far as I can) that all duties will be covered. In addition, if there were an inevitable delay and I knew I was going to be late, I could call the hospital and ask if the clinic were running on time, explain that I was running a little late and ask if the consultant would be willing to wait for me.

F

Task 6 I would leave until last. Although it is important to respect our colleagues and to ensure whenever possible we keep appointments that we have made, seeing a drug rep is a non-patient task and my own health would definitely take priority over this. I would apologise to the rep and ask them to rearrange an appointment with reception.

Task Prioritisation
Practice Exercise 3

Advanced

Task Prioritisation Exercise 3

Examination paper

You are a doctor based in primary care. You are at the end of your 4-month attachment and the partners allow you to see patients independently, asking for help whenever you need it.

It is Friday afternoon and there is one other doctor in the surgery. Your clinic list finishes early every Friday at 18:00 to allow you to attend an evening class. Today's class is the final one in the series before the summer holiday and you will receive your exam results.

It is now 16:45 and you still have a waiting room full of patients. You like to run to time. You receive 5 messages in succession.

1	The community Macmillan nurse calls. A terminal patient of yours needs to start a subcutaneous infusion of morphine. It has been agreed, but you need to write the prescription up and arrange for delivery to the house. The pharmacy closes at 17:00. The Macmillan nurse hands over to an on-call service at 17:00.
2	Your job application for specialist "run through" training is due to be submitted by the end of today. You still have some details to complete before sending it off by email.
3	The relative of a recently deceased patient has called asking for you to contact them about a request for a post-mortem examination by the coroner. Your colleague had reported the death to the coroner as the patient had died suddenly and had not seen a doctor recently.
4	The local pharmacist has called and would like to speak to you about a recent prescription that you have written.
5	There is a patient in reception who is waiting for a letter that you had promised to leave at reception by Friday afternoon at the latest. The receptionist calls to ask if you can write it now. The patient is agitated.

Justify how you would complete the tasks in the boxes below in the order that you would complete them. Remember that you need to leave to reach your class. A is the first task that you would complete. E is the last task that you would complete.

A

B

C

D

E

Other comments

Reflective learning

1. What three things did you find difficult about the exercise?

2. What one thing did you find easy about the exercise?

3. What two things have you learnt about yourself from completing this exercise?

4. What two things would you do differently next time?

Task Prioritisation Exercise 3

Discussion

Read the brief

Did you spend time reading the brief?

Who are you? Where are you based? What job are you doing?
How much time do you have left on your shift? Who is available to help you?

You know that you are working in General Practice. You know that you are not the only doctor, and have with you the rest of the General Practice team available. The brief mentions a pharmacist, doctor and a receptionist.

There are often other people present in General Practice.
Is there a medical student?
Does the practice have a nurse, counsellor or other allied staff? What about the practice manager?

Who could you use to help with each task?

<u>Message 1</u>

The community Macmillan nurse calls. You have only 15 minutes to resolve this before the pharmacy closes. Can the pharmacist help you? Would they be willing to stay open a little later to help you resolve this issue? Is there a district nurse who could help with the delivery of the prescription and setting up the device? Can the on-call Macmillan nurses help?

<u>Message 2</u>

You are the only person who can complete your application form. If things were quieter, or if the brief was hospital based, you could ask a colleague to cover you while you resolve this issue.

Message 3

Can the partner who certified the death and reported the case to the coroner help? If you were hospital-based, is there a bereavement officer who could talk to the family to explain the process and need for post-mortem.

Message 4

Could the receptionist call the pharmacist for you to explain that you are aware of his call and will respond as soon as you are able? Could the pharmacist come to you? The brief states that they close at 17:00.

Message 5

By justifying this in a way that suggests that the letter has definitely been written, you can ask the practice secretary, receptionist or manager to help with this task.

> *I always dictate my letters at the end of the surgery that it relates to. I know that the letter will definitely have been dictated and so would ask the practice secretary to check whether it had been typed.*

More information

In most of the messages there is little need for additional information.

The assessment criteria

Remember the assessment criteria? (See Figure 13 p.195.)

1 – Written skills

> If the assessor cannot read your writing, they will be unable to give you the marks that you deserve.
>
> Look at your writing. Can you read it?
> Is it clear?
> Do you understand what you have written down?
> Ask a colleague. Can they read it?

2 – Approach

Did you think about the tasks and messages before you started writing?
Did you make any logical notes?
Are there multiple scribbles on your paper because you changed your mind over and over again?
What could you do differently next time?
If you didn't make notes, try making them during the next practice exercise. You may find that it helps.
If you did make notes, did they help? Did they confuse you? Did you waste precious time making them?

3 – Thought process

Is your thinking and justification clear? Does it make sense?
Is it appropriate? Cross-check your justification with the ranking that you gave them.
Do you have multiple mistakes crossed out because you changed your mind?
What would you do differently next time? Is there something you could do to help clarify your thoughts?

Did you try splitting the messages into "patient", "extended patient" and "other"?

"Patient"

> Message 1: The community Macmillan nurse calls. A terminal patient of yours needs to start a subcutaneous infusion of morphine. It has been agreed, but you need to write the prescription up and arrange for delivery to the house. The pharmacy closes at 17:00. The Macmillan nurse hands over to an on-call service at 17:00.

> Message 5: There is a patient in reception who is waiting for a letter that you had promised to leave at reception by Friday afternoon at the latest. The receptionist calls to ask if you can write it now. The patient is agitated.

"Extended patient"

> Message 3: The relative of a recently deceased patient has called asking for you to contact them about a request for a post-mortem examination by the coroner. Your colleague had reported the death to the coroner as the patient had died suddenly and had not seen a doctor recently.

> Message 4: The local pharmacist has called and would like to speak to you about a recent prescription that you have written.

"Other"

> Message 2.
> Your job application for specialist "run through" training is due to be submitted by the end of today. You still have some details to complete before sending it off by email.

Remember that the brief states that you need to leave on time and have the added pressure of your class to think about.

By splitting the messages into these categories it often helps to clarify the general order that the messages should be ranked into.

4 – The emergency case

Did you recognise that there were two direct patient cases?

Only the Macmillan request is a true emergency case. The dignity and care of the dying is as important as the care of our living patients.

Did you put the patient first as suggested in the GMC guidance?
Are you a safe doctor?

5 – Ranking

Did you rank the tasks as requested?
Did you place the first message in box A and the last message in box E?
How did you fill them in? Did you decide on the obvious last and clear first task and then fill in the other boxes?
Did you fill in the boxes in order?

Whichever way you tried, did it work for you? Is it worth trying the exercise again approaching it in a different way?

Is your ranking appropriate?

Do the "patient-centred" tasks come before the "extended patient" tasks?

Do the "other" tasks rank lower down?

The one exception to this is message 2 – the need for you to spend time on the computer to complete your application process. Did you recognise the effect on you? How did you justify this?

One approach would be to recognise the failing and "mistake" within your answer:

> *I would usually ensure that anything as important as a job application for run through specialist training was completed well in advance of the deadline. There is no time limit attached to the deadline for application and so I assume that the online application can be submitted before midnight. I could therefore complete this task at home although I realise that it would be on my mind at work. I may need to miss my evening class to complete this task in time.*

Depending upon your justification, this "other" task is likely to have ranked last in your list.

Suggested ranking:

A 1	This is an obvious first task to complete. The patient is dying and we need to ensure our terminal care and quality of death is as good as it can be.
B 5 C 4	These are both "extended patient" cases and could be placed in any order. Should the pharmacist come first to show our respect for our colleagues? Should the agitated patient's letter come first? This will depend on your justification.
D 3	This is an "extended patient" message and, although we have a duty to the relatives of our deceased patients, this is likely to take a significant amount of time to sort out.
E 2	Your application form does need to be completed, but can be done in your own time.

6 – Teamwork

Did you use the team?
Did you think about clinical and non-clinical members of the multidisciplinary team?

Was the delegation appropriate?
Should you have completed more tasks yourself?
Should you have completed fewer tasks yourself?

Did you state anywhere that you would check to see if the tasks had been completed and get follow-up from your team members?

7 – Time management

Did you complete the exercise?
Was it much easier with only five tasks to think about?
Did you leave time for the reflective learning?

Are your answers to the first two stems very long with only a sentence for the other stems?
Did you rush the last few stems?

Did you have time to make a clear decision on the ranking or did you feel rushed into it?

How would you allocate the time better if you had to run the exercise again? Is there a better way?

8 – Effect on you

Did you acknowledge that the need to leave on-time to attend your evening class would have an effect on you?

There is a box for "other comments" in this question. You could have put in this box (or in the reflective learning part of the exercise) the need to re-evaluate how appropriate it is to have to rush off on a Friday evening to attend a class. This is the last one timetabled until after the summer. Would it be worthwhile trying to rearrange the class for another night of the week?

We need to have an adequate work-life balance and many would argue that we should always be able to leave on-time. If having this deadline to leave would affect your working day due to the added pressure, it may be worth assessing why leaving on-time is so difficult.

Why is it a pressure to leave on-time?
Are there enough doctors in the practice?
Are you being supported enough?
Are you overbooked?
Did you explain this in your answer?

9 – Reflective learning

Did you leave enough time for the reflective learning?
Did you complete all sections requested?
Did you learn anything from the exercise?
Were you open to the fact that we all make mistakes?
Did you acknowledge your limitations?
Did you appreciate what you did well?
Is there anything that you would do differently next time after experiencing this exercise?
Did you learn anything about yourself?

There is a great deal of information that you could write in each of the boxes provided. You need to decide which information is important in each case, justify how and why you would do each task and rank them according to your explanation. Remember: practise, practise, practise.

Task Prioritisation Exercise 3

Sample Answer

To help you to understand how to approach the written prioritisation question, read the following suggested appropriate answer. This is not a perfect answer and should not be regurgitated in an assessment situation. Remember that everyone will approach the question in a slightly different way and that there is no absolute answer. What is important is how you approach it, managing your time and ensuring that you are practicing safe medicine. What follows is one option of ranking for this task.

A

Message 1 would be my priority. This patient is terminally ill and the quality of care for the dying is as important as the care we give to the rest of our patients. I feel very strongly that the quality of a patient's death should be as good as it possibly can be. In view of the time restraint with both the pharmacy closing and the Macmillan nurse finishing at 17:00 I would need to attend to this quickly. Whilst I organised the prescription, I would ask the receptionists to call our local pharmacy explaining that an urgent prescription was on its way and asking them if they would stay open for us. My local pharmacy would often come and pick up the prescription in this type of case. I would also need to ensure that the request was communicated to the out of hours team of nurses and to the covering GP team in case problems arose overnight, and would ask the Macmillan nurse to assist me with this. If I had time at the end of my clinic and I knew the patient well, I would also like to go and see the patient once the pump had been sited to ensure that both the patient and the family were happy.

B

> Message 4 is a non-acute patient-related task and also takes into account our respect for our colleagues. I would want to attend to this as soon as I could, as I know it is late in the day and the pharmacy is due to close. This is likely to be a quick telephone call. If there was going to be a delay in talking to the pharmacist I would ask the receptionist to call, explaining that I was busy and could call them as soon as I could, asking for any further information on who the patient was and what the concern was to enable me to deal with this efficiently.

C

> Message 5 also has low clinical urgency but the patient is agitated and I would therefore like to ensure I dealt with it as soon as I could. I always dictate my letters at the end of the surgery that they relate to, so I know that the letter will be in the system somewhere. I would ask reception, the secretary or the practice manager to help determine whether my dictated letter had been typed and, if so, to print off a copy for me to sign. As this was being investigated I would pass on my apologies to the patient and try to alleviate their agitation. I would hope that this would be resolved quickly and efficiently, preventing this developing into a complaint by using effective patient communication.

D

> Message 3 is a non-patient task as the patient has died. I am aware that we still have a duty of care to the relatives of our deceased patients and I also know how important it is to communicate well in these situations to help the relatives manage their grief appropriately. This task is going to need to be addressed sensitively and a significant time allocated to it to be able to deal with it properly. On a rushed Friday afternoon I am not sure that I would be effective in resolving all of their issues and I would therefore, in the first instance, ask the secretary/ receptionist to contact the relatives offering a double appointment for Monday morning to be able to talk to them face to face. I would try to have a brief conversation with them over the telephone during the afternoon to alleviate any immediate anxiety and explain that the partner of the practice had reported the death and that I would be unable to answer their questions fully at that time. I would need to communicate with the partner to get the full information required to help them before their appointment. An alternative approach would be to ask the partner in question (if they were in the practice) to contact the relatives to help out.

E

Task 2 is a non-patient task and, although not finishing my application form would have an impact on me, I would have time to complete this task at home at the end of my clinic assuming that the submission deadline of "the end of the day" was midnight. I would usually ensure that my application forms were completed well in advance of any set deadline to prevent this situation arising, but clearly this time I have not managed to do this. I am aware that I also have an evening class to get to which appears to be an important class to attend. I would need to decide what was more important: my application form and future job, or my evening class. I would probably on balance stay at work until my application form was completed and sent before leaving to attend the class.

Other comments

Knowing I had an evening class to attend would add extra pressure to my Friday afternoon surgery. I know how important my work-life balance is, but if the class were impacting on my ability to perform at work I would need to rethink the timing of the class. This is to be the last one of the term, and I would therefore think hard before applying to attend the course at the same time again.

I would ensure that I was better prepared in future with regard to my application forms. Work is a huge part of our lives and in the current climate of job difficulties I would want a well-planned, timed and structured application to show me to my best ability in order to ensure my greatest possible success at shortlisting.

Task Prioritisation Practice Exercise 4

The 10-minute OSCE

The 10-minute OSCE

The following practice exercise is an example of the type of question that you will encounter if your selection centre runs a 10-minute OSCE assessment. The principle in how to answer them is exactly the same as described above in practice questions 1-3 but no justification is required.

The 10-minute OSCE exam paper will usually consist of five separate prioritisation situations. Each situation will have approximately four tasks or messages. You must complete all five situations in the allocated 10 minutes. It is worth trying to complete one of the exercises under timed examination conditions.

If you know that your deanery does not run the 10-minute assessment you can still use the following question to practice ranking alone, or you can draw out an answer sheet and use each stem as a separate 20-minute question by ranking and justifying your answers in the way described above.

The marking of this type of question is usually based on an "ideal" answer.

If you match the ideal answer you will score 5/5.
If you match 3-4 of the rankings you will score 3/5.
If you match 2 or fewer of the rankings you will score 0/5.

There is usually a clear "emergency" case. If you fail to rank this as number 1 you will score less, often losing all the marks and scoring 0/5.

Remember to split the tasks into "patient", "extended patient" and "other". The ranking will usually reflect this order.

Remember the effect on you.

Task Prioritisation Exercise 4

Examination paper

Rank the following tasks in the order that you would perform them. You have 10 minutes to complete five questions.

1 is the first task that you would complete.
5 is the last task that you would complete in each section.

Q1. You are a doctor based in A&E.

    a. A patient is having severe haematemesis and has collapsed with a blood pressure of 60/40.
    b. A patient has died and the nurses want you to certify the death.
    c. A stable elderly lady has been in A&E for 3 hours and 50 minutes. You need to refer her to elderly care before she "breeches" the 4-hour wait rule.
    d. You need to go to the library to pay a fine on an overdue book.
    e. You need to take some blood gasses from a patient with pancreatitis. The surgeons are aware of the patient and you are awaiting their review.

Ranking

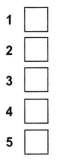

1
2
3
4
5

Q2. You are a surgical SHO/F2 doctor and on call.

a. You need to attend theatre to assist your Registrar with a routine appendicectomy.
b. You have been asked to attend A&E to review an emergency patient with suspected ruptured AAA (abdominal aortic aneurysm).
c. A patient on ITU needs a surgical review for possible small bowel obstruction.
d. The Consultant on call has left a message for you to contact him. He is unable to reach the Registrar.
e. A ward patient needs to be reviewed prior to discharge. They are well.

Ranking

1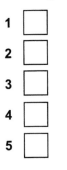

2

3

4

5

Q3. You are an F2/ SHO doctor on call for medicine.

a. The coronary care unit (CCU) has called. They have a patient who needs to be seen. The nurses have noticed runs of ventricular tachycardia (VT) on the monitor. The patient appears well and has a pulse and good blood pressure.

b. The arrest bleep goes off. A call has been put out on the orthopaedic ward.

c. A patient wants to self-discharge from the ward. They are post-overdose and have been reviewed by Psychiatry as no further suicide risk.

d. A&E needs you to attend and review a young asthmatic. The patient is unwell and may need HDU.

e. The pharmacy needs you to contact them to double-check a patient's medication that you have written for discharge.

Ranking

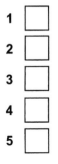

1

2

3

4

5

Q4. You are an SHO/ F2 doctor covering the obstetrics and gynaecology on call.

    a. There is a suspected ruptured ectopic pregnancy in A&E. You have been asked to attend.

    b. Your Registrar has called you. They are about to start a Caesarean section and would like you to assist.

    c. An antenatal patient wants to be discharged and needs a letter.

    d. You have to finish your audit project to present at the departmental meeting tomorrow morning.

    e. A midwife calls for you urgently. A patient on labour ward is having a severe postpartum haemorrhage. (PPH)

Ranking

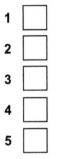

1

2

3

4

5

Q5. You are an F2/ SHO doctor in primary care.

    a. You have just been asked to plan a teaching session for the medical students attached to the practice. The session starts in 2 hours.

    b. The heath visitor is concerned about a child she has just seen in her clinic and would like to talk to you.

    c. The practice manager needs to talk to you about the on-call rota.

    d. The practice nurse has called. She would like some advice about a child who is due for their immunisation. They are allergic to eggs and have severe eczema.

    e. The receptionist calls. There is a patient on the line with chest pain.

Ranking

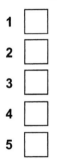

1

2

3

4

5

Task Prioritisation Exercise 4

Discussion

Time management

You had approximately 2 minutes per question.
How did you manage the time?
Did you answer each question?
Did you feel rushed?
Were you able to think about each stem and make an appropriate decision?
How could you organise your time better next time?

Approach

Did you split the tasks into "patient", "extended patient" and "other"?
Is there any other approach that you could use to make the task easier next time?

Reflective learning

There is unlikely to be a formal section in reflective learning in this type of question but look at examples 1-3 to ensure that you are completely prepared.

Think about how you coped.
What was easy?
What was hard?
What (if anything) did you learn about yourself?
What would you do differently next time?

The ideal answer

<u>Q1</u>
1. a
2. e
3. c
4. b
5. d

The patient with haemetemesis in extremis is an emergency. This must rank first. A failure to put this first may result in a score of 0/5.

Patients with pancreatitis are often very sick and will need to be closely monitored. Another team is aware of the patient but, until they arrive, it is your responsibility to ensure the patient is cared for appropriately

The elderly patient needs to be transferred not only because of the 4-hour wait rule, but also for her own comfort and care. This does not rank as an emergency above the haematemesis and pancreatitis, but is more important than a patient who has died and needs certification of death.

It is important that we deal with our deceased patients as soon as we can to help the grieving process of the relatives. There is often a pressure on beds in A&E and certifying this patient as soon as possible will also help the department as a whole.

Your own needs in this case would come last. Paying a library fine would not impact on your ability to keep working.

Scoring

The ideal answer	5/5
If 3 of your answers match the ideal answer	3/5
If 1 or 2 answers match	1/5

BUT
If you failed to rank the haematemesis as number 1	0/5
If you failed to rank the pancreatitis as number 2	1/5

Q2.

1. b
2. c
3. a
4. d
5. e

A suspected ruptured AAA is a surgical emergency. These patients need to be urgently transferred to theatre. A prompt review is essential.

The patient in ITU is stable and being cared for in a safe environment. A prompt review is required but this can happen after the review of the AAA.

Assisting with an appendicectomy may be interesting for those interested in a surgical career but this is an operation that can be carried out by a single surgeon. The Registrar is scrubbed in theatre.

The Consultant message is for the Registrar who is unreachable. It may be urgent and we should always respond to our senior colleagues promptly showing them the respect that they deserve. This should not compromise patient safety.

The patient who needs to be reviewed prior to discharge is well and therefore not an emergency. It is important to review patients like this as quickly as we are able to ensure appropriate use of hospital beds and facilities. You may have ranked this before talking to your Consultant. This would be acceptable.

Scoring

1.b	or	1.b
2.c		2.c
3.a		3.a
4.d		4.e
5.e		5.d

Both are acceptable answers and would score	5/5
If 3 answers match	3/5
If 1 or 2 answers match	1/5
BUT if you failed to put the AAA as number 1	0/5

262

Q3.

1. b
2. d
3. a
4. e
5. c

The cardiac arrest bleep is your immediate priority. Failure to place this as number 1 would score 0/5 for the whole question.

The asthmatic in A&E sounds as though they are in a critical condition. Talk of HDU means that the patient may be peri-arrest. This requires urgent attention.

The patient on CCU is stable and already in a high dependency area with close monitoring. They need to be seen quickly, but the asthmatic is critically ill and would need stabilising first.

The pharmacy needs to ask about a discharge medication. This is for a planned discharge and the patient is probably waiting. A delay here may prevent another admission.

The self-discharge patient has been deemed stable and fit for discharge from a psychiatric point of view. Most overdoses are not reviewed by psychiatry until they are fit for medical discharge and so this would therefore be last on the list of priorities.

Scoring

The ideal answer	5/5
If 3 answers match	3/5
If 1 or 2 answers match	1/5

BUT
If you failed to put the arrest call as number 1	0/5
If you failed to put the asthmatic patient as 2 or 3	1/5
If you failed to put the CCU patient as 2 or 3	1/5

Q4.

1. e
2. a
3. b
4. c
5. d

The postpartum haemorrhage is an obstetric emergency and the Registrar is unavailable. The ectopic in A&E can be stabilised and assessed by the A&E staff until you can attend.

The ruptured ectopic is a gynaecological emergency. The patient is being looked after by A&E staff who can stabilise and resuscitate until you arrive.

The Registrar needs your assistance, but it is possible to do a section with the theatre nurses' assistance. You would obviously attend as soon as you could.

The antenatal patient will need to be seen, but this is not an emergency.

The audit is important and may interfere with your work if you are preoccupied and anxious about finishing it. It should have been finished well in advance of the presentation tomorrow and you will have time at the end of your shift.

Scoring

The ideal answer	5/5
If 3 answers match	3/5
If 1 or 2 answers match	1/5

BUT

If you failed to put the postpartum haemorrhage as number 1	0/5
If you failed to put the ruptured ectopic as number 2	1/5

Q5.

1. e
2. d
3. b
4. c
5. a

The patient on the line with chest pain is a clinical emergency. They may be in the middle of an acute myocardial infarction. Assessment of the symptoms over the phone is quick and easy. If there is any doubt they should call 999.

The child who is in the surgery and about to have an immunisation is a "patient" task. You need to find out what vaccination they are having as an atopic child (eczema) with an egg allergy could have an anaphylactic reaction.

The health visitor is concerned. If it were a life and death situation then they would contact social services or the police directly, so this is likely to be for advice. This can therefore be classed as an "extended patient" task and be ranked third.

Talking to the practice manager about the on-call rota may be a quick task to complete. The on-call rota impacts on patient care (particularly if the practice manager needed you to cover the on-call that afternoon) and should be completed before a non-patient task.

The teaching of medical students is important and the GMC guidance states that we all have a duty to educate the next generation of doctors. This task was given to you at short notice and it is therefore not your fault that you have a short time frame for preparation.

Scoring

The ideal answer	5/5
If 3 answers match	3/5
If 1 or 2 answers match	1/5
BUT if you failed to put the chest pain first	0/5

Conclusion

There is often a clear number 1 and clear number 5 task to complete. Adding the time pressure in an examination setting makes this type of exercise much harder. Practise, practise, practise!

Section 7

Final Words

Summary of topics covered

There are three exercises that you will encounter during your Stage 3 assessment centre:

1. The patient simulation (role-play) exercise,
2. The group discussion,
3. The written (prioritisation) exercise.

Remember that these can occur in any order on the day. They will not necessarily be presented to you in the order that is in the book

Having read the book, practised the exercises and integrated what you have learnt from the book into your everyday working life, you should now feel better prepared and less apprehensive about your upcoming assessment centre.

If you remember nothing from the book at all, please try to remember at least the key words associated with each of the three exercises:

1. The patient simulation (role-play) exercise   LISTEN
                                                      BELIEVE THAT IT IS REAL

2. The group discussion   TEAM
                                                      HOW, NOT WHAT

3. The written (prioritisation) exercise   THREE TYPES OF TASKS
                                                      EFFECT ON YOU
                                                      TIME

Over the following pages there are summaries of topics covered by this book and a list of other possible topics that could come up. Remember that you do not have to be an expert at everything. It is acceptable to say you do not know in the group discussion and patient simulation exercises.

Be a safe doctor. Communicate well in the written and in the spoken form to both colleagues and patients and you should do well.

This book is not designed to tell you "what" to say or "how" to say it. This book is designed to be your guide to practicing the skills that are listed in the personal specification.

Practise, practise and practise again.

Prepare well and try to enjoy the assessment centre.

Good luck!

Summary of proposed assessment criteria

Role play/ Patient simulation

1. Creating a safe environment
2. Introduction and putting the patient at ease
3. Active listening and encouragement
4. Relevant psychosocial information
5. Expectations of the patient including any hidden agenda
6. Clinical questioning
7. Explanation and differential diagnosis
8. Working diagnosis and management plan
9. Patient choice
10. Checking the patient's understanding
11. Follow-up and review as required
12. Actor patient's general impression
13. Body language and physical interaction
14. Remaining calm under pressure

Prioritisation/ written exercise

1. Written skills
2. Approach
3. Thought process
4. The emergency case
5. Ranking
   - Patient
   - Extended Patient
   - Others
6. Teamwork
7. Time management
8. Effect on you
9. Reflective learning

Group discussion

Communication
- Clear
- Concise
- Uses appropriate language
- Interactive
- Respectful and listening
- Avoids confrontations

Participation
- Actively engages
- Constructive
- Makes self heard
- Assertive
- Confident
- Coherent

Teamwork
- Works with the team
- Shows awareness of others
- Smoothes difficulties with other colleagues
- Encourages others to participate
- Supports and respects others
- Adapts to the needs of the group
- Shows leadership whenever appropriate
- Facilitates the discussion whenever appropriate

Time management
- Played role in ensuring good time management

Problem solving
- Contributes to the resolution of the problem
- Thinks laterally
- Adaptable
- Receptive to other ideas
- Handles conflict well

Overall impression
- Good response from other candidates
- Productive discussion
- General question answered
- Follow-up and forward planning dealt with

Body language and voice
- Good eye contact
- Good body language
- Appropriate attitude
- Appropriate volume of voice
- Articulate and clear

Summary of topics covered within the text

Role play
Communication
Difficult colleagues
Difficult patients
Breaking bad news
Psychosocial components to patient care
Confidentiality
Consent
Capacity and competence
Admitting mistakes
Probity

Group discussion
Probity
Gifts from patients
Underperforming colleagues
Complaints
Refusal of treatment, capacity and competence, Fraser guidelines
Organisational skills
Fund-raising
Conflicts of interest
Ethical principles
Ill health in our colleagues
Documentation
Reporting
Staffing
European Working Time Directive
GMC guidance
Multidisciplinary team
Termination of pregnancy

Prioritisation
Reflective learning
The safe doctor – recognising an emergency
Asking for help
Our own health

Summary of other topics that could be used

This list is endless as in theory any issue from primary or secondary care could be covered in the assessment centre. Most subjects you will be familiar with if you have worked in the NHS and are a UK graduate. If you have not worked in the NHS I would suggest you do some reading about working in the NHS and look at current issues in the medical press.

Audit
Clinical governance
Medical pay and the press releases e.g. the "GP on £250,000!"
Opting in and out of organ donation
NHS polyclinics in General Practice
Private vs. NHS care
Summary care record (the national computer database for patient records)
Information technology within the NHS (Choose and book, PACS etc.)
Out of hours cover in General Practice
Practice-based commissioning
GPs with specialist interests
The effect of the Shipman enquiry on current medical practice
The changes in medical education (e.g. MTAS, Specialist training)
Teaching
GMC guidance
Quality and Outcomes Framework in General Practice (QOF)

You do not need to be an expert in any of these topics. Simply be aware of what they mean and be prepared to admit your limited knowledge in the group discussion or role play if they arise.

References

The following publications and references are mentioned in the text.

1. Certification Unit of the Royal College of General Practitioners
   http://www.rcgp.org.uk/the_gp_journey/certification.aspx

2. Citizens Advice Bureau
   www.citizensadvice.org.uk

3. Cruse Bereavement Care
   www.crusebereavementcare.org.uk

4. European Working Time Directive
   www.dh.gov.uk. DH-4075554.pdf Guidance in the working time regulations 2003. Implementation for doctors in training. Page 7

5. Foundation competencies
   www.foundationprogramme.nhs.uk

6. General Medical Council
   www.gmc-uk.org

7. *Good Medical Practice* (2006). GMC publications
   www.gmc-uk.org/guidance/good_medical_practice/index.asp

8. GPST personal specification
   www.mmc.nhs.uk/pages/specialties-personspecs

9. National Recruitment Office for General Practice Training
   www.gprecruitment.org.uk

10. Postgraduate Medical Education and Training Board (PMETB)
    www.pmetb.org.uk

11. Relate counselling
    www.relate.org.uk

12. Royal College of General Practitioners
    www.rcgp.org.uk

Summary of abbreviations used

CAB	Citizens Advice Bureau
CCT	Certificate of Completion of Training
CCU	Coronary care unit
CPR	Cardiopulmonary resuscitation
CV	Curriculum vitae
EMQ	Extended matching question
FY1	Foundation year 1 doctor
FY2	Foundation year 2 doctor
GMC	General medical council
GP	General practice
GPST	General Practice Specialist Training
HDU	High Dependency Unit
ITP	Innovative training post
ITU	Intensive therapy unit
MCQ	Multiple-choice question
MDU	Medical Defence Union
MPS	Medical Protection Society
MTAS	Medical Training Application Service
NHS	National Health Service
NSAIDs	Non-steroidal anti-inflammatory drugs
OSCE	Observed structured clinical examination
OHP	Overhead projector
OT	Occupational therapy
PACS	Picture Archiving and Communications System
PALS	Patient Advice and Liaison Service
PCT	Primary care trust
PMETB	Postgraduate Medical Education and Training Board
PPH	Postpartum haemorrhage
PRHO	Pre-registration house officer
QOF	Quality and Outcomes Framework
RCGP	Royal College of General Practitioners
SHO	Senior house officer
ST	Specialist training
UK	United Kingdom
VT	Ventricular tachycardia

Index of figures in the text

Role play

Figure 1. Poor positioning of chairs. The table is a barrier between the doctor and the patient

Figure 2. Suggested alternative set-ups. The desk is no longer a barrier. Work out your own preferred distance between the patient and doctor chairs. See what feels comfortable. Try without a desk if that is more comfortable for you.

Figure 3. Summary of proposed assessment criteria for role play

Figure 4. Suggested time for each role play

Group discussion

Figure 5. Typical room set-up (assuming 4 candidates and 4 assessors)

Figure 6. Typical room set-up (assuming 4 candidates and 2 assessors)

Figure 7. Summary of proposed assessment criteria for group discussions

Figure 8. Suggested time for each group discussion

Prioritisation

Figure 9. Type 1 prioritisation paper

Figure 10. Type 2 prioritisation paper

Figure 11. Suggested approach to ranking order in the prioritisation exercise

Figure 12. Team support

Figure 13. Suggested assessment criteria for the written prioritisation exercise

ISCMEDICAL
Interview Skills Consulting